Probability and Statistics

Written by
Wendy Osterman

Editor: Alaska Hults
Illustrators: Carmela Murray and Corbin Hillam
Designer: Carmela Murray
Cover Designer: Moonhee Pak
Art Director: Tom Cochrane
Project Director: Carolea Williams

Table of Contents

Table of Contents

Table of Contents

Introduction

How do you help your students keep newly acquired math skills and review the concepts they've already mastered? Provide them with reinforcement and review through the activities in *Probability and Statistics.* Regular reinforcement of learned skills helps students gain a deeper understanding of the material as well as learn more difficult concepts with greater ease in the classroom.

Probability and Statistics offers an additional component of skill review that most books like it do not: a complete explanation of the target skill. For this reason, the book can function as enrichment for advanced students who are ready to go further in probability and statistics, as well as remediation for students who didn't understand the skill the first time it was presented.

Probability and statistics are important skill concepts that students need in order to be successful at higher levels of math. However, since your schedule is likely jam-packed, it can be almost impossible to schedule classroom time to go further or provide more practice with the skills you have presented. *Probability and Statistics* provides a clear explanation of each element of the math strand in language accessible to middle-grade students. The explanations do not talk down to students or go over their heads with extensive lingo. Frequent examples from real life help students understand how probability and statistics are daily used around them.

Probability and Statistics is a terrific supplement to any mathematics program. Assign a practice page immediately following a lesson or later for review. Used regularly and in page order, the book can even replace part of your math instruction for this strand. We recommend that if you use any part of the book as first instruction for the skill or concept, you progress from the start of the book to the back. Concepts build on each other, and the exercises in the statistics section assume knowledge of skills learned in the probability section. Each ready-to-go probability or statistics activity is an effective way to recharge or enrich students' skills. So get started today!

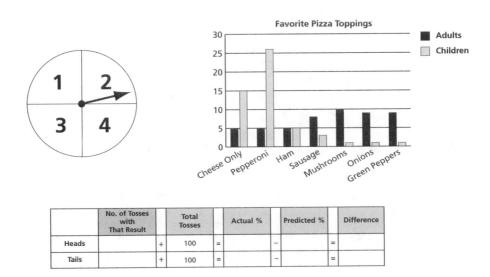

	No. of Tosses with That Result		Total Tosses		Actual %		Predicted %		Difference
Heads		÷	100	=		–		=	
Tails		÷	100	=		–		=	

Name _____   **Date** _____

Talk the Talk
Introducing Probability Vocabulary

- **Probability** measures how likely it is that an event will occur.
- An **experiment** is a method used to collect information.
- A **simple event** is the most basic outcome of an experiment. There might be more than one.
- The **sample space** is the collection of all possible simple events for a single experiment. Sometimes this is recorded in an oval.

Experiment	Flip a coin
Simple events	Heads up Tails up

Sample space

(Heads   Tails)

Examine each experiment. Describe the experiment. Answer the questions.

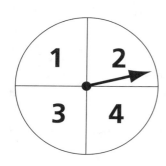

Experiment: _____

1 What are the simple events? _____

2 How many simple events are there? _____

3 What would you record in the sample space for this spin?

_____

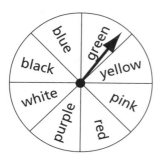

Experiment: _____

4 What are the simple events? _____

5 How many simple events are there? _____

6 What would you record in the sample space for this spin?

_____

Probability and Statistics © 2005 Creative Teaching Press

Hop, Skip, Jump
Identifying Elements of a Probability Experiment

Use what you know about hopscotch to answer the questions.

Experiment: _____

1 What are the simple events? _____

2 How many simple events are there? _____

_____

3 What would you record in the sample space for this toss?

_____

4 Which simple event seems most likely?

_____

Experiment: _____

5 What are the simple events? _____

6 How many simple events are there? _____

_____

7 What would you record in the sample space for this toss?

_____

8 You would have to be very lucky to get which event?

_____

Continue to page 2.

Probability and Statistics © 2005 Creative Teaching Press

Hop, Skip, Jump
Page 2

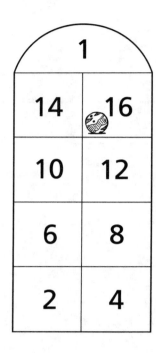

	1	
14	16	
10	12	
6	8	
2	4	

Experiment: _____

9 What are the simple events? _____

10 How many simple events are there? _____

_____

11 What would you record in the sample space for this toss?

_____

12 Are you more likely to land on odd or even numbers in

this experiment? _____

Experiment: _____

13 What are the simple events? _____

14 How many simple events are there? _____

_____

15 What would you record in the sample space for this toss?

_____

16 Are you more likely to land on a prime number or a
composite number in this experiment?

_____

Probability and Statistics © 2005 Creative Teaching Press

Name _____   Date _____

Roll It
Identifying Elements of a Probability Experiment

Use what you know about quarters and dice to answer the questions.

Experiment: _____

1 What are the simple events? _____

2 How many simple events are there? _____

3 What would you record in the sample space for this toss?

_____

4 Are you more likely to land on heads? Why or why not?

_____

_____

Experiment: _____

5 What are the simple events? _____

6 How many simple events are there? _____

7 What would you record in the sample space for this toss?

_____

8 Would it be lucky to get ten 6s in a row? Why or why not?

_____

_____

Continue to page 2.

Probability and Statistics © 2005 Creative Teaching Press

Roll It

Page 2

Experiment: _____

9 What are the simple events? _____

10 How many simple events are there? _____

_____

11 What would you record in the sample space for this toss?

_____

12 How are the simple events different from flipping just

one quarter?_____

_____

_____

Experiment: _____

13 What are the simple events? _____

14 How many simple events are there? _____

_____

15 What would you record in the sample space for this toss?

_____

16 How are the simple events different from rolling just one die?

_____

_____

Probability and Statistics © 2005 Creative Teaching Press

Name _____   Date _____

Likely or Lucky?
Exploring Likelihood

Discuss with a partner.
- If the weatherman says that rain is likely today, and then it rains, is that lucky?
- If your father serves pizza for dinner almost every Wednesday night, is it likely that he'll serve pizza for dinner this Wednesday? Why?
- You have a golf ball stuck on the roof. Your brother has a kickball stuck on the same roof. Both balls roll to the edge of the roof. You and your brother decide to try to knock the balls down. Who is likely to hit and knock their ball down first? Why? If your brother knocks his ball down first, was that likely or lucky? Explain.

Answer the questions based on your understanding of the words *likely* and *lucky*. Be ready to discuss your reasoning in class.

1 Do you think it is likely to roll three dice and have all three land with a 6 up? Why or why not?

2 Do you think it would be likely or lucky to have heads land faceup on a coin toss after calling "heads"? Why or why not?

3 How do you determine if something is likely?

4 Name a time that you were lucky, and explain what made it lucky.

5 How do you think that the words *likely* and *lucky* are related?

6 Explain why you think the following statement is true or false: You are lucky if an event happens that is unlikely.

Probability and Statistics © 2005 Creative Teaching Press

Name _____ Date _____

Likely, Not Likely
Estimating Probability

Every day we make decisions based on what we think is likely. Sometimes it is helpful to figure out *exactly* how likely. But sometimes we only need to *estimate* the likelihood of an event. For example, usually Coach Stevens has the kids on his soccer team line up and count off *1, 2, 1, 2,* and so on, until the last player. Then he has all the 1s play on one team and all the 2s play on the other. If Ben and Milo want to be on the same team, should they stand next to each other or place another team member between them? It is probable, or likely, that Coach Stevens will have the kids count off the way he usually does. So, to be on the same team, the boys should convince another player to stand between them.

Read each situation. Write *likely* or *not likely,* and then write a sentence or two that explains your answer.

1 Carolyn takes the bus across town to her ballet lessons every Monday afternoon. She knows that usually $\frac{2}{3}$ of the people waiting at her stop want to get on the same bus she does. She also knows that the bus, which holds 40 people, is usually half full already. Carolyn arrives at the bus stop late. There are already 18 people waiting, and here comes the bus! She is last in line. Is she likely to get a seat anyway? Explain your reasoning.

_____

_____

2 Carlos has two brothers and two sisters. Every Friday night, his mother brings home a treat for the whole family. To be fair, she rotates the treat among her children's favorites. For example, last week the family had flan, which is a kind of pudding that Carlos's youngest sister adores. Carlos always hopes the treat is chocolate ice cream. If the family just had chocolate ice cream two weeks ago, is it likely or not likely that this Friday will be chocolate ice cream again? Explain your reasoning.

_____

_____

Probability and Statistics © 2005 Creative Teaching Press

Continue to page 2.

3 Katya has just moved with her family to a part of the United States where it almost never rains during the summer. Her mother explains that where they live, it has not rained in August in over ten years! Katya wakes up on August 10 to overcast skies and asks her mother if it will rain today. Her mother smiles and says, "No, the clouds will burn off soon, and it will be another sunny, clear day." Is her mother likely or not likely to be correct?

_____

_____

_____

4 Ally's new puppy is a lot of fun. Her constant tail wagging has even won over Ally's gruff father. However, the puppy does have one truly bad habit: she digs in the backyard. In the last week, she has dug up an entire garden bed of tulip bulbs, three holes in the landscaping around two different trees, one sprinkler head, and 15 random holes in the grass. In fact, the puppy usually digs at least two new holes each time she is allowed to go into the backyard alone. Ally's father has implemented a new rule that the puppy must be watched whenever she goes out into the yard in order to stop the digging. Ally sees the puppy staring hopefully out the window into the backyard. Ally is tempted to let the puppy out "just for a few minutes." Is it likely that the puppy will go into the backyard and NOT dig?

_____

_____

_____

5 Every Tuesday is trash day on Mulberry Street. For the last 15 weeks, the garbage truck has come by between the hours of 2:00 p.m. and 4:00 p.m. Is it likely that the garbage truck will come by this Tuesday at 8:00 a.m.? Is it possible?

_____

_____

_____

Probability and Statistics © 2005 Creative Teaching Press

Name _____   **Date** _____

How Likely?
Expressing Probability

Probability is the likelihood that a simple event will occur. The actual outcome often does not exactly match the probability, but it will be close.

Probability may be expressed as a fraction or as a decimal. To express the likelihood of an event as a fraction, write the number of simple events *desired* as the numerator. Write the *total* events in the sample space as the denominator.

Experiment: Die roll
Simple events desired: 1, 3
All possible simple events: 1, 2, 3, 4, 5, 6

$$\frac{\text{Number of simple events desired}}{\text{Total number of simple events}} = \frac{2}{6}$$

1 What is the probability of rolling an odd number on the die?

Simple events desired: _____

All possible simple events: _____

$$\frac{\text{Number of simple events desired}}{\text{Total number of simple events}} = \underline{}$$

2 What is the probability of rolling a number greater than 4?

Simple events desired: _____

All possible simple events: _____

$$\frac{\text{Number of simple events desired}}{\text{Total number of simple events}} = \underline{}$$

Continue to page 2.

How Likely?

Page 2

3 What is the probability of rolling a number greater than 0?

Simple events desired: _____

All possible simple events: _____

$\dfrac{\text{Number of simple events desired}}{\text{Total number of simple events}} = \underline{\quad}$

Would you say this is likely?   Why or why not?

4 What is the probability of rolling a prime number?

Simple events desired: _____

All possible simple events: _____

$\dfrac{\text{Number of simple events desired}}{\text{Total number of simple events}} = \underline{\quad}$

5 What is the probability of rolling a number less than 2?

Simple events desired: _____

All possible simple events: _____

$\dfrac{\text{Number of simple events desired}}{\text{Total number of simple events}} = \underline{\quad}$

Probability and Statistics © 2005 Creative Teaching Press

Name _____   Date _____

So Far, So Good
Investigating Real-Life Probability

Some real-life events are very complex, and it can be difficult to exactly measure the probability of a simple event happening. Weather is an excellent example of a complex event—there are so many factors that can affect how it behaves. Others are less complex. For example, in a box of Marshmallow Chunkies cereal, the marshmallows come in four colors: red, blue, yellow, and green. The manufacturer says that the typical box has about equal amounts of each color. So the experiment to calculate the *approximate* probability of choosing a green marshmallow from the box would look like this:

Simple event desired: green marshmallow
All possible simple events: red, blue, green, or yellow marshmallow

$$\frac{\text{Number of simple events desired}}{\text{Total number of simple events}} = \frac{1}{4}$$

1 You are holding one blue shoe. Five shoes remain in your closet. There is only one other blue shoe in your closet. If you reach into your dark closet, grab any shoe, and wear it to school, what is the probability that you will be wearing two blue shoes?

Simple events desired: _____

All possible simple events: _____

$$\frac{\text{Number of simple events desired}}{\text{Total number of simple events}} = \underline{}$$

2 You decide to throw all six shoes back in your closet. Half of them are left shoes. What is the probability that you will grab a left shoe if you reach in and grab any shoe?

Simple events desired: _____

All possible simple events: _____

$$\frac{\text{Number of simple events desired}}{\text{Total number of simple events}} = \underline{}$$

Continue to page 2.

So Far, So Good
Page 2

3 Let's say the shoe you chose in the last question was indeed a left shoe. Now, what is the probability that you will choose a right shoe if you reach in and grab another shoe?

Simple events desired: _____

All possible simple events: _____

$$\frac{\text{Number of simple events desired}}{\text{Total number of simple events}} = \underline{}$$

4 After determining that none of the shoes in your closet fit, you go out and purchase two new pairs of shoes. All of the shoes are in a heap on the closet floor. If you reach in and pull out one shoe, what is the likelihood that it will fit?

Simple events desired: _____

All possible simple events: _____

$$\frac{\text{Number of simple events desired}}{\text{Total number of simple events}} = \underline{}$$

5 Your brother needs to buy you a birthday present but can't think of anything you like. Looking in your closet, he decides you must really like shoes. He notices that none of the shoes are red, so he buys you a pair of red shoes that fit. What are the chances when you reach in that you will grab one of the birthday shoes?

Simple events desired: _____

All possible simple events: _____

$$\frac{\text{Number of simple events desired}}{\text{Total number of simple events}} = \underline{}$$

Is It Worth It?
Investigating Real-Life Probability

Probability helps people decide whether it is worth it to play certain games or activities. For example, Raul and Marie go to the state fair. They want to win a goldfish. At the first booth, they can win the fish by throwing a Ping-Pong ball through one of ten holes. At the second booth, they can win the fish by picking up a plastic duck with a green sticker on the bottom. There are 50 ducks altogether. Ten ducks have green stickers. Let's compare the odds of winning each game.

Game 1

Simple event desired: a Ping-Pong ball in a hole
All possible simple events: 1 win, 9 losses

$$\frac{\text{Number of simple events desired}}{\text{Total number of simple events}} = \frac{1}{10}$$

So probably only about one toss in ten will win.

Game 2

Simple event desired: a duck with a green sticker
All possible simple events: 10 wins, 40 losses

$$\frac{\text{Number of simple events desired}}{\text{Total number of simple events}} = \frac{10}{50} = \frac{1}{5}$$

So probably about one pick in five will win.
Raul and Marie have a better chance of winning at the second booth.

Find the probability of winning the following games.

1 For this game, the winner picks a blue card from a pack of 20 cards. There are 3 blue cards in all.

Simple event desired:

All possible simple events:

Probability of winning:

2 For this game, the winner picks an odd-numbered card from a pack of 20 cards, which are numbered from 1 to 20.

Simple event desired:

All possible simple events:

Probability of winning:

Probability and Statistics © 2005 Creative Teaching Press

Continue to page 2.

Is It Worth It?

Page 2

3 For this game, the winner picks a blue stone from a bag of 40 stones. There are 5 blue stones in all.

Simple event desired:

All possible simple events:

Probability of winning:

4 For this game, each player tosses a stone on a large grid where each box is labeled with a number from 1 to 20. The winner tosses the stone on a prime number.

Simple event desired:

All possible simple events:

Probability of winning:

5 For this game, each player stands in the center of a circle of five archery targets. The winner must hit the bull's-eye on at least three of the targets. Assume that all players are equally skilled and able to hit a bull's-eye with a bow and arrow.

Simple event desired:

All possible simple events:

Probability of winning:

6 For this game, players walk in a circle while music plays. There are 15 evenly spaced plates on the floor. There are 5 blue plates, 3 green plates, 6 yellow plates, and 1 red plate. The winner stops on the red plate.

Simple event desired:

All possible simple events:

Probability of winning:

Name _____ **Date** _____

Certainly Impossible
Investigating Certain and Impossible Events

Spin a 5

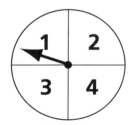

What is the probability of spinning a 5?

It is *impossible* to spin a 5 because the spinner does not contain this number. Spinning 5 is not a possible simple event.

$$\frac{\text{Number of simple events desired}}{\text{Total number of simple events}} = \frac{0}{4}$$

Choose a Boy

A teacher randomly chooses a boy from his all-male class of 20 students to answer a question. **What is the probability that the student chosen is a boy?**

It is *certain* that the student chosen will be a boy because there are no alternative simple events. All possible events will result in a boy being chosen.

$$\frac{\text{Number of simple events desired}}{\text{Total number of simple events}} = \frac{20}{20}$$

It is unusual to find certain and impossible probability problems on math tests, but they are common in real life!

Read each situation, and write *certain* or *impossible* to describe it.

1 You are playing Dominos with your 3-year-old brother using 9-dot dominos. Each player earns the number of points on the open end of each domino he or she places on the board. Your brother can match the dots, but he is still a little fuzzy with his number identification. He places one domino and says that he gets "20!" How likely is this?

2 Your brother is thirsty. He announces he wants a juice box. All the juice boxes are apple juice. He places his hands on his hips and announces, "I only want the apple ones!" You laugh. Are you laughing because his choice is certain or impossible?

3 Surprise! You open your closet to find that your cat has given birth to seven kittens! An examination reveals that all the kittens are males. Your uncle offers to take three of the kittens to work as mousers on his farm. What is the probability that he will choose a boy kitten?

4 You choose a number from the following list: 2, 3, 5, 7, 11, 13, 17, 19. What is the probability that the number will be a *composite* number?

Probability and Statistics © 2005 Creative Teaching Press

Name _____   Date _____

Real-Life Sample I
Understanding Probability in Context

Newspapers are a good source for finding real-life examples of probabilities.

Find one picture or article that includes probabilities. Cut it out and glue it below. Then, briefly describe the experiment, simple events, and sample space.

Probability and Statistics © 2005 Creative Teaching Press

Look Again
Identifying Missing Information

 Fernando's class is going on a field trip to the sea lion rescue center. Fernando wants to sit next to his best friend, Henry, on the bus. What is the probability that this will happen?

Puzzled? That's because part of the information is missing! We are never told how many students there are in Fernando's class. If there are only 6 students in the class, then there is a better chance that Fernando will sit next to Henry than if there are 36 students in the class.

For each problem, describe the information that must be supplied in order to calculate the probability.

1 Your mom packs your lunch. What is the probability that your sandwich will be ham and cheese?

2 You need to get a 6 on the spinner to win a game you are playing. What is the probability that you will get a 6?

3 You want to get a higher die roll than your friend. What is the probability that this will happen?

4 You are throwing a ball for your dogs. The dogs are the same size, age, and health. You have noticed before that they seem to get the ball about the same number of times each. What is the probability that Lady, one of the dogs, will catch the ball on the next throw?

5 It is time to feed your lizard. You place some crickets, worms, and beetles in a bowl and place the bowl in the lizard's vivarium. What is the probability that the lizard will eat one of the worms first?

Probability and Statistics © 2005 Creative Teaching Press

Marbles
Pursuing Probability Practice

 There are 20 marbles in the bag. Three marbles are green. Six marbles are yellow. One marble is black. Five of them are purple. The remaining marbles are purple and gold swirled together. Assume the narrow opening means you cannot see into the bag when you reach in to pick a marble. After you pick a marble, you look at the color, note it, and then put the marble back in. So each time you pick, there are always 20 marbles.

Read and solve each problem.

1 What is the probability that you will pick a solid yellow marble?

2 What is the probability that you will pick a solid green marble?

3 What is the probability that you will pick a swirled marble?

4 What is the probability that you will pick a solid black marble?

5 What is the probability that you will pick a solid purple marble?

6 What is the probability that you will pick any solid marble?

7 What is the probability that you will pick a solid red marble?

8 What is the probability that you will pick a marble with gold on it?

9 What is the probability that you will pick a yellow or green marble?

10 What is the probability that you will pick a marble with any purple on it?

Next Step!
Converting Fractions to Decimals

Convert $\frac{1}{2}$ to a decimal.

Divide the numerator by the denominator. $2\overline{)1.0}^{\,0.5}$

Convert each fraction to a decimal.

1 $\frac{1}{5}$

2 $\frac{3}{12}$

3 $\frac{15}{50}$

4 $\frac{24}{60}$

5 $\frac{1}{20}$

6 $\frac{2}{40}$

7 $\frac{4}{5}$

8 $\frac{24}{30}$

9 $\frac{1}{10}$

10 $\frac{4}{4}$

11 $\frac{5}{8}$

12 $\frac{2}{5}$

13 $\frac{3}{20}$

14 $\frac{6}{75}$

Probability and Statistics © 2005 Creative Teaching Press

Messy Decimals
Converting Fractions to Repeating Decimals

Some fractions convert to repeating decimals. Convert $\frac{1}{3}$ to a decimal.

Divide the numerator by the denominator. $3\overline{)1.000}$ gives $0.33\overline{3}$

A line over the last digit(s) of a decimal means that the decimal repeats those numbers from that point on.

Convert each fraction to a repeating decimal.

1 $\frac{2}{6}$

6 $\frac{5}{24}$

2 $\frac{5}{18}$

7 $\frac{7}{27}$

3 $\frac{4}{12}$

8 $\frac{4}{33}$

4 $\frac{5}{9}$

9 $\frac{8}{24}$

5 $\frac{4}{21}$

10 $\frac{5}{54}$

Perfect Percents
Converting Decimals to Percents

Convert the decimal to a percent.

Multiply the decimal by 100.

$0.5 \times 100 = 50$

So, $\frac{1}{2} = 0.5 = 50\%$

Solve.

1 $\frac{1}{5} = 0.2 = $

2 $\frac{3}{12} = 0.25 = $

3 $\frac{15}{50} = 0.3 = $

4 $\frac{24}{60} = 0.4 = $

5 $\frac{1}{20} = 0.05 = $

6 $\frac{2}{40} = 0.05 = $

7 $\frac{4}{5} = 0.8 = $

8 $\frac{24}{30} = 0.8 = $

9 $\frac{1}{10} = 0.1 = $

10 $\frac{4}{4} = 1 = $

11 $\frac{5}{8} = 0.625 = $

12 $\frac{2}{5} = 0.4 = $

13 $\frac{3}{20} = 0.15 = $

14 $\frac{6}{75} = 0.08 = $

Probability and Statistics © 2005 Creative Teaching Press

Approximate Percents
Converting Repeating Decimals to Percents

To convert a repeating decimal to a percent, add one extra step to the usual method.

$$\frac{1}{6} = 0.16\bar{6}$$

Round 0.166 to the nearest hundredth. $0.166 \approx 0.17$

Multiply by 100.

$0.17 \times 100 = 17$

So, $\frac{1}{6} = 0.166 \approx 17\%$

Solve.

1 $\frac{2}{6} = 0.333 \approx$ _____ $\times 100 =$

2 $\frac{5}{18} = 0.2777 \approx$ _____ $\times 100 =$

3 $\frac{4}{12} = 0.333 \approx$ _____ $\times 100 =$

4 $\frac{5}{9} = 0.555 \approx$ _____ $\times 100 =$

5 $\frac{4}{21} = 0.190476 \approx$ _____ $\times 100 =$

6 $\frac{5}{24} = 0.208333 \approx$ _____ $\times 100 =$

7 $\frac{7}{27} = 0.259259 \approx$ _____ $\times 100 =$

8 $\frac{4}{33} = 0.1212 \approx$ _____ $\times 100 =$

9 $\frac{8}{24} = 0.333 \approx$ _____ $\times 100 =$

10 $\frac{5}{54} = 0.0925925 \approx$ _____ $\times 100 =$

Name _____   Date _____

Probability Percents
Practicing Probability Percents

 With the toss of a coin, there are only two possible outcomes—heads or tails. Heads is one of two possible outcomes. The probability of getting heads is $\frac{1}{2}$, which is equal to 0.5 or 50%. This means that *approximately* 50% of the time, heads will be faceup in a coin toss. We say "approximately" because in real life the outcome may not be exactly 50%. We could also say that the *likelihood* of getting heads is 50%, or your *chance* of getting heads is 50%.

Find the percent of probability for each situation.

1 What is the probability of getting a 1 or a 2 on a roll of a die?

$$\frac{2}{6} = \qquad \approx \qquad \times 100 =$$

2 What is the probability of getting a number greater than 3 on a roll of a die?

$$— = \qquad \times 100 =$$

3 What is the probability of getting a number greater than or equal to 3 on a roll of a die?

$$— = \qquad \approx \qquad \times 100 =$$

4 What is the probability of getting a number greater than 4 on a roll of a die?

$$— = \qquad \approx \qquad \times 100 =$$

Continue to page 2.

Probability Percents
Page 2

Assume the die has eight sides for the following problems.

5 What is the probability of getting a 7 on a roll of this die?

$$\underline{\quad} = \quad \approx 100 =$$

6 What is the probability of getting a number greater than 4 on a roll of this die?

$$\underline{\quad} = \quad \approx 100 =$$

7 What is the probability of getting a number greater than or equal to 3 on a roll of this die?

$$\underline{\quad} = \quad \approx 100 =$$

8 What is the probability of getting a number less than 4 on a roll of this die?

$$\underline{\quad} = \quad \approx 100 =$$

Use what you know about fractions to estimate the percentage of each whole that is darkly shaded.

9 Estimated fraction: _____ Estimated percent: _____

10 Estimated fraction: _____ Estimated percent: _____

11 Estimated fraction: _____ Estimated percent: _____

12 Estimated fraction: _____ Estimated percent: _____

Probability and Statistics © 2005 Creative Teaching Press

What Are the Chances?
Practicing Probability Percents

With the roll of a standard die, there are only six possible outcomes: 1, 2, 3, 4, 5, or 6. Rolling a 1 is one of the six possible outcomes. The probability of rolling a 1 is $\frac{1}{6}$, which is about 17 percent. Approximately 17 percent of the time, the roll of a die will result in a 1. Or the likelihood of rolling a 1 is about 17 percent. Or your chance of rolling a 1 is about 17 percent.

Find the percent of probability for each situation.

1 A bag of 40 marbles has 8 white marbles. What is the probability of picking a white marble?

2 A bag of 40 marbles has 3 white, 2 red, and 5 green marbles. The remaining marbles are clear. What is the likelihood of picking a red marble?

3 A bag of 75 marbles has 8 white, 10 red, and 20 green marbles. The remaining marbles are clear. What is the chance of picking a red or a green marble?

4 A bag of 100 marbles has 25 white, 25 red, and 36 green marbles. The remaining marbles are clear. What is the probability of picking a white marble?

5 A bag of 40 marbles has 13 white, 2 red, and 9 green marbles. The remaining marbles are clear. What is the likelihood of picking a red or a white marble?

Continue to page 2.

Probability and Statistics © 2005 Creative Teaching Press

What Are the Chances?

Page 2

6 A bag of 75 marbles has 8 white, 10 red, and 20 green marbles. The remaining marbles are clear. What is the chance of picking a clear marble?

7 A bag of 40 marbles has 12 white, 2 red, and 9 green marbles. The remaining marbles are clear. What is the probability of picking any marble other than a clear one?

Read each situation, and answer the questions.

8 A bag of 60 marbles has 30 white, 20 red, and 5 green marbles. The remaining marbles are clear. The likelihood of picking marbles of which two colors is equal?

9 A bag of 50 marbles has 5 red, 7 blue, 35 orange, and 3 green marbles. In drawing a marble from the bag 100 times, a red marble was picked 14 times. What was the likelihood of a red marble being picked? Is this more or less than the actual number?

10 A bag of 60 marbles has 8 red, 9 blue, 10 orange, and 33 green marbles. In drawing a marble from the bag 100 times, a blue marble was picked 15 times. What was the likelihood of a blue marble being picked? Is this more than, less than, or equal to the actual number?

11 A bag of 60 marbles has 8 red, 9 blue, 10 orange, and 33 green marbles. In drawing a marble from the bag 100 times, an orange marble was picked 13 times. What was the likelihood of an orange marble being picked? Is this more or less than the actual number?

12 A bag of 60 marbles has 15 marbles of each color (i.e., red, blue, orange, and green). In drawing a marble from the bag 100 times, a red marble was picked 20 times. What was the likelihood of a red marble being picked? Is this more or less than the actual number?

Flip It!
Comparing Actual Results to a Prediction

 With the toss of a coin, there are only two possible outcomes—heads or tails. Heads is one of two possible outcomes, so the probability of getting heads is $\frac{1}{2}$. The probability of getting tails is the same. We can also say that we have a 50% chance of getting either heads or tails. Now it's time to compare our predictions to the real results! The more tosses of the coin, the more accurate the results; so you are going to flip a coin 100 times.

Flip the coin. Record the result of each toss as a tally mark in the appropriate column. After 100 tosses, find the sum of the tally marks, and compare your results to the probability.

Heads	Tails

Now, check your prediction, and answer the questions.

	No. of Tosses with That Result		Total Tosses		Actual %		Predicted %		Difference
Heads		÷	100	=		−		=	
Tails		÷	100	=		−		=	

1 How close were your actual results to the probability? How did the results differ from your expectations?

2 Are you convinced that probability is somewhat close to real-life results? Why or why not?

Probability and Statistics © 2005 Creative Teaching Press

Reality Check
Comparing Actual Results to a Prediction

 With the roll of a die, there are six possible outcomes: 1, 2, 3, 4, 5, or 6. A 4 is one of six possible outcomes, so the probability of rolling a 4 is $\frac{1}{6}$. We can also say that we have about a 17% chance of rolling a 4. Now it's time to compare our predictions to the real results! The more rolls of the die, the more accurate the results; so you are going to roll a die 100 times.

Roll the die. Each time you roll a 4, record the result as a tally mark. Check off each box to track your rolls. Then, find the sum of the tally marks, and compare your results to the probability.

ROLLS	□□□□□□□□□□□□□□□□□□□□
	□□□□□□□□□□□□□□□□□□□□
	□□□□□□□□□□□□□□□□□□□□
	□□□□□□□□□□□□□□□□□□□□
	□□□□□□□□□□□□□□□□□□□□
4s	

Continue to page 2.

Reality Check
Page 2

Now, check your prediction, and answer the questions.

No. of 4s Rolled		Total Rolls		Actual %		Predicted %		Difference
	÷	100	=		–	17%	=	

1. How close were your actual results to the probability? How did the results differ from your expectations?

2. Are you convinced that probability is somewhat close to real-life results? Why or why not?

3. Jimmy rolled a die 100 times. On 80 of the rolls, he got a 2. What are your thoughts about the likelihood of the results? Do you think that the die is "fair"?

4. Erin rolled a die 50 times. On 9 of the rolls, she got a 6. What are your thoughts about the likelihood of the results? Do you think that the die is "fair"? (Hint: To find the actual percent of 6s rolled, use the equation in the table above but use 50 for the total number of rolls.)

Probability and Statistics © 2005 Creative Teaching Press

Real-Life Sample II
Understanding Probability in Context

Conduct your own experiment. Record the experiment, simple events, and sample space below. Find the probability of each simple event. Then, find the actual results of the experiment, and record them below. Be creative—no rolling a die or tossing coins.

Experiment:

Simple events:

Sample space:

Desired event:

Probability of desired event:

Actual outcome:

Name _____ **Date** _____

Spin It!
Exploring Variables in Probability

 With this spinner, the probability of getting a 1, 2, 3, or 4 is exactly the same: $\frac{1}{4}$. This is true because each section of the spinner is exactly the same size.

 On this spinner, the sections are unequal. The 4 takes up $\frac{1}{2}$ of the spinner. Therefore, the probability of getting a 4 is actually $\frac{1}{2}$ with this spinner. The 1 takes up $\frac{1}{4}$ of the spinner; therefore, the probability of getting a 1 is $\frac{1}{4}$. The 2 and 3 each take up $\frac{1}{8}$ of the spinner. Therefore, the probability of getting a 2 or a 3 is $\frac{1}{8}$.

Follow the directions.

❏ Cut out the spinner and arrow at the bottom of the page. To make the spinner sturdier, glue it to a paper plate before adding the arrow.

❏ Use a brass fastener to attach the arrow.

❏ Color in the spinner so that it has the following properties:

Red: $\frac{1}{4}$ Blue: $\frac{1}{8}$

Orange: $\frac{1}{8}$ Yellow: $\frac{1}{8}$

Green: $\frac{1}{4}$ Purple: $\frac{1}{8}$

❏ Spin the spinner several times, and keep a tally of the results on the Spin It! Record Sheet (see page 37). Determine if your spinner is a "fair" spinner.

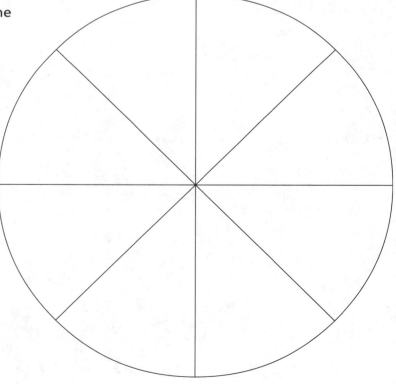

Probability and Statistics © 2005 Creative Teaching Press

Continue to page 2.

Spin It! Record Sheet

Page 2

Red	Blue	Green	Orange	Yellow	Purple

Are the actual results similar to the probabilities?

Probability and Statistics © 2005 Creative Teaching Press

Building Spinners
Exploring Variables in Probability

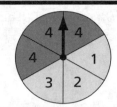 On this spinner, the sections are unequal. The 4 takes up $\frac{1}{2}$ of the spinner. Therefore, the probability of getting a 4 is actually $\frac{1}{2}$ with this spinner. The 1, 2, and 3 each take up $\frac{1}{6}$ of the spinner; therefore, the probability of getting one of these numbers is $\frac{1}{6}$.

Color each spinner to create the following probabilities.

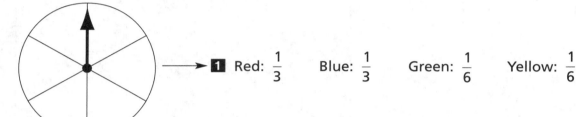

1 Red: $\frac{1}{3}$ Blue: $\frac{1}{3}$ Green: $\frac{1}{6}$ Yellow: $\frac{1}{6}$

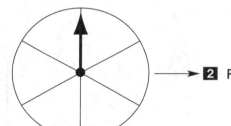

2 Red: $\frac{1}{6}$ Blue: $\frac{1}{6}$ Green: $\frac{1}{6}$ Orange: $\frac{1}{6}$ Yellow: $\frac{1}{3}$

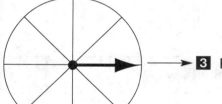

3 Red: $\frac{1}{8}$ Blue: $\frac{1}{8}$ Green: $\frac{1}{4}$ Orange: $\frac{1}{2}$

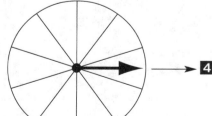

4 Red: $\frac{1}{5}$ Blue: $\frac{3}{10}$ Green: $\frac{1}{10}$ Orange: $\frac{2}{5}$

Probability and Statistics © 2005 Creative Teaching Press

Real-Life Sample III
Understanding Probability in Context

Reading a spinner is a lot like reading a pie graph.

Design and create a spinner of your own. Use at least five different colors or numbers. Then write the probability of getting each color or number.

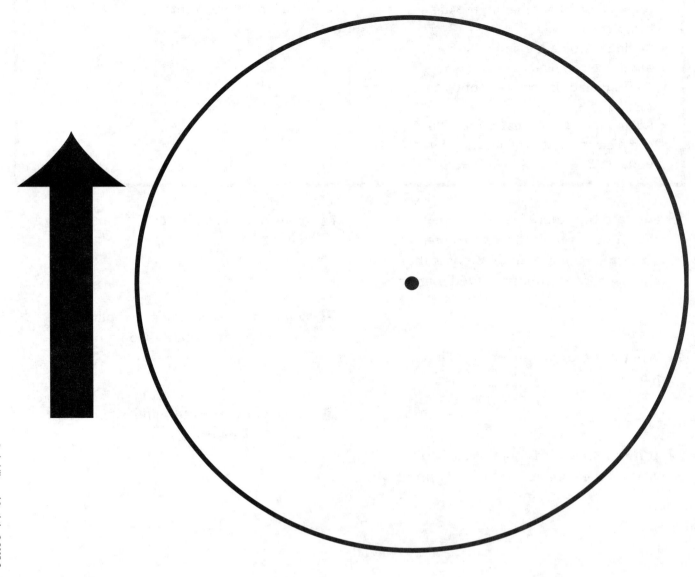

Probability and Statistics © 2005 Creative Teaching Press

Name _____ Date _____

Looking for Opposites
Understanding Complementary Events

Complementary events are opposite events.	
Examples of complementary events	**Example of an event that is NOT complementary**
• Rolling an even number on a die and rolling an odd number on the die are complementary. • Rolling a 2 on a die and rolling a 1, 3, 4, 5 *and* 6 are complementary. • Tossing heads is complementary to tossing tails. • Rolling a number greater than 3 is complementary to rolling less than or equal to 3.	• Rolling a 2 and rolling a 3 are not complementary events.

1 Suppose that there is a bag of marbles that contains the following colors: red, blue, green, and orange. What is the complement of choosing a red marble?

2 What is the complement of rolling a 1 on a die?

3 You have five cards numbered 1 to 5. What is the complement of choosing a 4?

4 What is the complement of a baby boy being born?

5 What is the complement of rolling a number greater than a 4 on a die?

6 Explain how to determine if two events are complementary.

Probability and Statistics © 2005 Creative Teaching Press

Name _____ Date _____

Nice Complement
Identifying Complementary Events

Event 1: Choosing a number between 1 and 10 from a bag
Event 2: Choosing a number between 11 and 20 from a bag
Are these complementary events? It is not possible to tell. We need to know if the numbers are in the same bag! We also need to know what the desired event is. If we want to choose only a 4, then all the other numbers are the complementary event.

Answer the questions based on the Venn diagram.

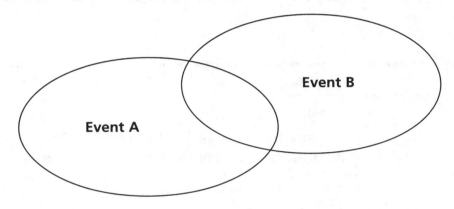

1 Are Events A and B complementary? Why or why not?

2 State the complement of Event A.

3 State the complement of Event B.

4 Make up your own example of a complement. Draw a Venn diagram to illustrate your example.

Probability and Statistics © 2005 Creative Teaching Press

Name _____ Date _____

Sketch It Out
Understanding Tree Diagrams

Compound events are a combination of events occurring consecutively. What if we wanted to find the probability of tossing heads then tails OR tails then heads in consecutive tosses? This is a compound event. It can be expressed in a tree diagram.

heads, tails
heads, heads
tails, heads
tails, tails

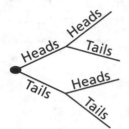

The first "branch" of the "tree" shows the first flip. The second level of branches shows the second flip. A tree diagram can be used to find all possible compound events.

Create a tree diagram for each problem.

1 Suppose that a family has two children. Draw a tree diagram to illustrate the possible combinations of the genders of the two children.

2 You shuffle and place in a pile three cards: 1 red, 1 blue, and 1 yellow. Draw a tree diagram to illustrate the possible results of pulling a card from the pile three times in a row (always replacing the card and shuffling again after each pull).

3 You have four dogs: a poodle, a Labrador, a schnauzer, and a mixed breed. Every time you open the front door, they all go racing out! Draw a tree diagram to show all the possible results for which dog is first out the door on a day in which you open the door *twice*. (Hint: To save space, you may want to use *P* for poodle, *L* for Labrador, and so on.)

Probability and Statistics © 2005 Creative Teaching Press

Advanced Probability
Calculating Probabilities for Compound Events

Now that you understand how a tree diagram works, let's revisit our problem. We want to find the probability of tossing heads and then tails OR tails and then heads in consecutive tosses. This was the tree diagram we made:

These are our desired outcomes:

heads, tails

tails, heads

These are the complementary outcomes:

heads, heads

tails, tails

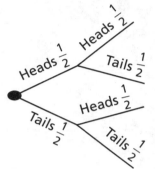

$$\frac{1}{2} \times \frac{1}{2} = \frac{1}{4}$$

$$\left.\begin{array}{l}\frac{1}{2} \times \frac{1}{2} = \frac{1}{4} \\[4pt] \frac{1}{2} \times \frac{1}{2} = \frac{1}{4}\end{array}\right\} \frac{1}{4} + \frac{1}{4} = \frac{1}{2}$$

$$\frac{1}{2} \times \frac{1}{2} = \frac{1}{4}$$

We can tell by looking at the tree diagram that each of the outcomes shown above has an equal probability of $\frac{1}{4}$. By adding the two desired outcomes together, we can estimate that we would achieve our desired outcome about half of the time.

Draw a tree diagram to illustrate each problem and solve.

1 A man and his wife are walking arm in arm to the store when they come to a gate too narrow to go through together. Assuming that they do not have a preference for who goes first, what is the probability that the wife goes through first on both the way there and the way back?

Continue to page 2.

Advanced Probability

Page 2

2 Fraternal twins are the most common kind of twins. These twins look no more or less alike than any two siblings. The most common combination of fraternal twins is the boy/girl set. Assume that a mother is as likely to have a boy as a girl. Use a tree diagram to show why the mother of twins is more likely to have a boy/girl set than a boy/boy set or a girl/girl set.

3 Creamy Crispy Donuts is having free-donut day, and they sure are busy. The donut shop speeds up service by telling people that they have to take what they are given. That is, people get a donut free, but they do not get to pick which kind. There are four different kinds of donuts. There are equal amounts of each kind in the box from which the Creamy Crispy Donut worker is pulling donuts. What is the likelihood that the next three people will get the same donut?

Probability and Statistics © 2005 Creative Teaching Press

Name _____   Date _____

Once More, with Fractions
Multiplying Fractions to Find Compound Probability

You can use what you know about fractions or decimals to figure out the probability of compound events, with or without a tree diagram. For instance, in our example of the coin toss
where the desired events are heads then tails OR tails then heads, we can obtain the probabilities
by multiplying. In this example, all of the simple event probabilities are $\frac{1}{2}$. Therefore, all the
compound events are $\frac{1}{2} \times \frac{1}{2} = \frac{1}{4}$. Each of the compound events has an equal probability of $\frac{1}{4}$.
However, there are two desired outcomes, so that means combining two probabilities: $\frac{1}{4} + \frac{1}{4} = \frac{1}{2}$.

Solve.

1 Mama Cat has three kittens (A, B, and C). Today they twice left their box to go explore.
Multiply to find the probability that Kitten A left the box first both times.

2 You shuffle and place in a pile three cards: 1 blue, 1 green, and 1 yellow. Draw a tree
diagram to illustrate the possible results of pulling a card from the pile three times in a row
(always replacing the card and shuffling again after each pull). Then, multiply and add to
find the probability that you will pull a green card at least two out of the three times.

Continue to page 2.

Once More, with Fractions

Page 2

3 You flip a coin three times. Illustrate the possible results. Multiply to find the probability that the coin will land heads up three times in a row.

4 Out of a bag of 30 marbles, there are 10 green marbles. What are the chances you'll draw a green marble three times in a row if you put the marble back in the bag after recording each result?

5 A bookstore is handing out free copies of books from your favorite series. You can only get one free book when you get to the front of the line, but you can stand in line as many times as you want. There are equal amounts of four different books. What is the probability that you will get a different book each time you go through the line if you go through the line four times?

6 You have a spinner with three sections. You spin it five times. What is the probability that it will land on the same section five times in a row? Show your math.

7 To win the raffle, you have to have a ticket with numbers that match the numbers drawn from a hat. There are nine tickets (labeled 1 to 9) in the hat. After a ticket is drawn, it is read and then put back in the hat to be pulled again. What is the chance that the first number on your ticket matches the first number that is drawn from the hat? What is the chance that the first two numbers on your ticket match the first two numbers drawn? What is the chance that the numbers on your ticket match all three numbers that are drawn?

Probability and Statistics © 2005 Creative Teaching Press

Name _____   Date _____

Not Equal
Multiplying to Find Compound Probability with Unequal Fractions

Why multiply to find a compound probability when you can just draw a tree diagram to "see" it? Because the tree diagram only works when all the chances are equally likely. For example, it would not work for this spinner:

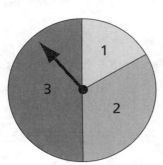

Probability of Spinning

$$1 = \frac{1}{6}$$

$$2 = \frac{1}{3}$$

$$3 = \frac{1}{2}$$

We can still multiply the individual probabilities to find their compound probability. For example, the likelihood that we would spin a 2 and then a 3 is: $\frac{1}{3} \times \frac{1}{2} = \frac{1}{6}$. The chance that we'd spin a 1 and then a 2 is $\frac{1}{6} \times \frac{1}{3} = \frac{1}{18}$; $\frac{1}{18}$ is a lot smaller than $\frac{1}{6}$. And that makes sense, given that you are basically asking, What are the chances that the spinner does not land at all in the left half of the spinner AND does land in the smallest space on the spinner?

Use multiplication to solve.

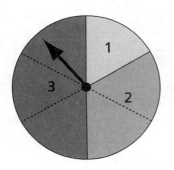

1 Find the probability of spinning a 1 and then a 3.

2 Find the probability of spinning a 3 and then a 3.

3 Which event in Problems 1 and 2 is more likely? Does that make sense? Why or why not?

Not Equal

Page 2

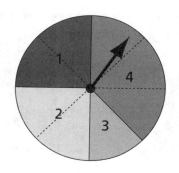

4 Find the probability of spinning a 1 and then a 2.

5 Find the probability of spinning a 3 and then a 4.

6 Find the probability of Problem 5 occurring, as a percent.

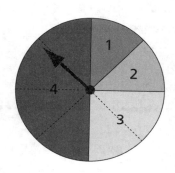

7 Find the probability of spinning a 1 and then a 2.

8 Find the probability of spinning a 3 and then a 4.

9 Find the probabilities of Problems 7 and 8 occurring, as percents.

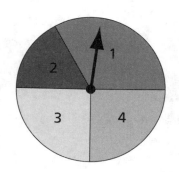

10 Find the probability of spinning a 1 and then a 2.

11 Find the probability of spinning a 3 and then a 4.

12 Find the probability of spinning a 1, as a percent.

Probability and Statistics © 2005 Creative Teaching Press

The Glider
Understanding Unequal Probabilities

Joey bought a toy glider. He wanted to determine the probability of the glider flying more than 15 feet, or less than or equal to 15 feet. He conducted an experiment by flying the glider 100 times. For 15 out of 100 times, it went less than or equal to 15 feet. He created this chart:

Event	Probability
> 15 ft.	$\frac{85}{100} = \frac{17}{20}$
≤ 15 ft.	$\frac{15}{100} = \frac{3}{20}$

We want to determine the probability of the glider going less than or equal to 15 feet twice in a row. We can start by listing all the possible compound events for two flights.

Possible Events
Glider flying ≤ 15 ft., then glider flying ≤ 15 ft.
Glider flying ≤ 15 ft., then glider flying > 15 ft.
Glider flying > 15 ft., then glider flying ≤ 15 ft.
Glider flying > 15 ft., then glider flying > 15 ft.

We are only really interested in the first compound event. So we calculate probability by using the fractional probability of the glider flying ≤ 15 feet ($\frac{3}{20}$). That equation would look like this: $\frac{3}{20} \times \frac{3}{20} = \frac{9}{400}$. Therefore, the probability is $\frac{9}{400}$. This means that for every 400 times that Joey flies the glider, he will get the outcome of the plane flying ≤ 15 feet twice in a row about 9 times.

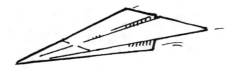

The Glider

Page 2

Use Joey's data to complete the problems.

1 Create a tree diagram to display the compound event of flying the glider two times in a row.

2 Find all possible probabilities of flying the glider two times in a row.

3 If Joey is happiest when the glider goes a long distance, do the statistics predict that Joey will usually enjoy his glider? Or do the statistics predict that he will quickly become disappointed in its performance?

Probability and Statistics © 2005 Creative Teaching Press

A Combination of Things
Introducing Combinations

There are five marbles in a bag: one red, one orange, one green, one blue, and one yellow. If you pull out two marbles at a time, how many different color combinations could you get? Assume you replace the marbles after each pull.

An arrangement of objects where order is not important is called a **combination**. In a combination, pulling one yellow and one red object is the same as pulling one red and one yellow object. There is an algebraic formula that will help us find the number of combinations for any number of items. It looks like this:

$$_nX_r = \frac{n!}{(n-r)!\,r!}$$

(where *n* is the number of items and *r* is the number taken each time)

But when the number of items is quite small, then it is just as easy to make a list and count. The only rule is a simple one: be careful not to list the same combination twice.

R = red	O = orange	G = green	B = blue	Y = yellow
RO				
RG	OG			
RB	OB	GB		
RY	OY	GY	BY	

Create a list to find the combinations for each event.

1 You have six crayons. If you take out three crayons at a time, how many color combinations are there? (The list was started for you.)

RED	ORANGE	YELLOW	BLUE	GREEN	PURPLE
ROY					
ROB					
ROG					
ROP					

Continue to page 2.

A Combination of Things
Page 2

2 You have six dogs. Every time you open the front door, two escape. In what combinations might the dogs run out the door?

Poodle   **Labrador**   **Schnauzer**   **Great Dane**   **Terrier**   **Chihuahua**

3 You are on a long drive with your siblings. Feeling bored, you decide to play a game. Your dad empties out his pocket change and places it in a sock. You and your siblings each reach in, pull out a coin, and open your hand to see if it is heads or tails. Given that your dad has at least one penny, one nickel, one dime, and one quarter in the sock, what are the possible combinations for the first three coins pulled out?

Probability and Statistics © 2005 Creative Teaching Press

How Many Ways?
Finding Combinations

There are five marbles in a bag: one red, one orange, one green, one blue, and one yellow. If you pull out two marbles together, how likely are you to pull out a red and an orange marble?

R = red	O = orange	G = green	B = blue	Y = yellow
RO				
RG	OG			
RB	OB	GB		
RY	OY	GY	BY	

There are ten different combinations when the marbles are drawn from the bag two at a time. Each is equally likely to occur, so any of the combinations has a $\frac{1}{10}$ probability.

Find the combinations, and calculate the probability for each event.

1 You roll two dice. Complete the chart, and find the probability of rolling a 1 and a 6.

1, 1			
1, 2	2, 2		
1, 3	2, 3	3, 3	
1, 4	2, 4	3, 4	4, 4
1, 5	2, 5	3, 5	
1, 6	2, 6	3, 6	

2 You toss four coins in the air. What is the probability that the coins will all land heads up?

Probability and Statistics © 2005 Creative Teaching Press

Continue to page 2.

How Many Ways?
Page 2

3 Three people are needed to work each day at a construction site. There is a group of part-time construction workers who share the job. To keep things fair, every evening they pull names from a hat to determine who will work the next morning. What are the chances that Emma, Al, and Ben will work tomorrow?

Al   Ben   Chad   Dan   Emma   Fred   Gigi   Hanna

4 Natalie wears a uniform to school every weekday. She has in her closet a pair of trousers, a skirt, a jumper, a white top with short sleeves, a white top with long sleeves, a blue top with short sleeves, and a blue top with long sleeves. What are the combinations for her two-piece outfits on any given day? (Remember, drawing an illustration can help you think through a problem.) If her mother randomly picks out an outfit for her this morning, what are the chances she ends up in a jumper with a blue long-sleeved shirt?

Probability and Statistics © 2005 Creative Teaching Press

Permutations
Understanding Combinations in Which Order Matters

Mama Cat has three kittens (A, B, and C).
Today they twice left their box to go explore.

The last time we visited Mama Cat, we asked how likely it would be that Kitten A left the box first both times. Another common question is, How many different ways are there for the kittens to leave the box? There is an algebraic formula that will help us find this for any number. It looks like this:

$$_nP_r = \frac{n!}{(n-r)!}$$

(where n is the number of items and r is the number taken each time)

But when the number of items is quite small (five or less) and you are going to take each one at a time (first A, then B, and then C), then it is just as easy to make a list and count. The only rule is a simple one: be careful not to list the same order twice.

ABC	BAC	CAB
ACB	BCA	CBA

There are six different permutations for the three kittens to leave the box. A **permutation** is a combination in which the order matters.

Create a list to find the permutations for each event.

1 How many different ways can you order the letters *F, A, T,* and *E*?

2 In how many ways can Chris, Alex, Vesna, Jacob, and Jose stand in line?

Continue to page 2.

Permutations
Page 2

3 How many four-digit numbers can you make by arranging the numbers 9, 1, 2, and 8?

4 Cara, Ian, and Sam are in a race. In how many different ways can they cross the finish line?

5 You have a penny, a nickel, a dime, and a quarter inside a bag. List all the ways you can pull three coins from the bag.

6 In how many different ways can you pull the following tiles from a bag? Show your work.

Probability and Statistics © 2005 Creative Teaching Press

What Are the Chances of Order?
Exploring Permutations and Probability

Mama Cat has three kittens (A, B, and C). Today they twice left their box to go explore. How many different ways are there for the kittens to leave the box?

ABC	BAC	CAB
ACB	BCA	CBA

There are six different permutations for the three kittens to leave the box. Kitten personality aside, each event is equally likely to occur, so any of the combinations has a $\frac{1}{6}$ probability.

Create a list or picture to find the solution to each problem.

1 A game randomly scrambles the letters in *TEAM.* What are the chances that the new order will spell *MEAT?*

2 Chris, Alex, Vesna, Jacob, and Jose stand in line for lunch every day. What are the chances that the order today is Alex, Jacob, Jose, Vesna, and then Chris?

3 The following tiles are in a bag:

What are the chances of pulling them out in this order?

Continue to page 2.

What Are the Chances of Order?

Page 2

4 The following tiles are in a bag:

What are the chances of pulling them out in this order?

5 The following tiles are in a bag:

What are the chances of pulling them out in this order?

Probability and Statistics © 2005 Creative Teaching Press

Real-Life Sample IV
Understanding Probability in Context

Write a short essay that describes probability. Use probability vocabulary, but be sure to explain the term in your own words.

OR

Find a book about probability, or look up probability online (with an adult's permission) and find five facts or concepts that you have not already learned. Briefly describe each fact or concept.

_____

_____

_____

_____

_____

_____

_____

_____

_____

_____

_____

_____

Pickup Sticks?
Review

Stuck? Draw a picture or diagram to help you better understand the problem.

100 Sticks—Numbered

You dump the box of 100 numbered sticks on the floor. What is the probability that . . .

1 you pick up a stick with a multiple of 5?

2 you pick up a stick with a multiple of 10?

3 you pick up a stick with a multiple of 2?

4 you pick up a stick with a multiple of 8?

5 you pick up a stick with a multiple of 5 and 8?

6 you pick up a stick with a multiple of 5 or 8?

7 you pick up a stick with a multiple of 2, followed by another multiple of 2? (Assume you return the stick after the first pick.)

8 you pick up a stick with a multiple of 10, followed by a multiple of 2? (Assume you return the stick after the first pick.)

Probability and Statistics © 2005 Creative Teaching Press

Put On Your Thinking Cap!

Review

Stuck? Draw a picture or diagram to help you better understand the problem.

Solve.

1 What is the probability of tossing heads three times in a row with a coin?

2 What is the probability of tossing the same side three times in a row with a coin?

3 What is the probability of rolling a 1 two times in a row with a die?

4 What is the probability of rolling any number two times in a row with a die?

5 What is the probability of rolling a die two times, adding the rolls together, and getting a sum less than 3?

6 What is the probability of rolling a die two times, adding the rolls together, and getting a sum greater than 6?

7 What is the probability of rolling a die three times, adding the rolls together, and getting a sum greater than 6?

Donuts
Review

The experiment is to randomly pick a donut from a box that has the following six donuts: glazed, plain, sprinkles, double chocolate, chocolate frosted, and jelly.

Solve.

1 What are the simple events?

2 What is the sample space?

3 What is the probability of choosing a jelly donut? Express your answer as a fraction.

4 Convert the fraction from Question 3 to a percent.

5 What is the probability of choosing a donut that has some chocolate? Express your answer as a fraction.

6 Convert the fraction from Question 5 to a percent.

7 What is the complementary event of getting a plain donut?

Jelly Beans
Review

You have a bag of jelly beans. There are 10 white, 15 yellow, 25 red, 22 purple, 17 pink, and 11 black jelly beans in the bag.

Solve.

1 Give the probability for randomly picking each of the six colors of jelly beans, as a fraction and a percent:

Color	Probability (fraction)	Probability (%)
white		
yellow		
red		
purple		
pink		
black		

2 What color are you most likely to pick?

3 What color are you least likely to pick?

Name _____ **Date** _____

Six-Sided Die
Review

The experiment is to roll a six-sided die.

Solve.

1 How many simple events will there be?

2 What are the simple events?

3 What is the sample space?

4 What is the probability of rolling a 1? Write the answer as a fraction and a decimal.

5 What is the probability of rolling an even number? Write the answer as a fraction and a decimal.

6 What is the complement of rolling a 1?

Probability and Statistics © 2005 Creative Teaching Press

Definitions
Review

Next to each vocabulary word, write the letter of the definition. Notice that there are more definitions than vocabulary words.

1 Experiment _____

A. The likelihood that a sample space will occur

B. The method used to collect information

C. The likelihood that a simple event will occur

2 Simple Event _____

D. An event that is really easy to complete

E. Events that are kind to one another

F. A sampling of an area

3 Sample Space _____

G. Opposite events

H. The most basic outcome of an experiment

I. The collection of all experiments

4 Probability _____

J. Events that relate to one another

K. The collection of all possible simple events

5 Complementary Events _____

L. The likelihood that an experiment will occur

6 Use all five terms to tell about probability in your own words.

Name _____ Date _____

Spinners and Chocolate
Review

Identify what information is missing, or answer the question if all needed information is supplied.

1 You choose a blue marble from a bag. You know that there are 10 blue marbles in the bag. What is the probability of randomly picking a blue marble? State the probability or the missing information.

2 You have a box of 20 chocolates that all look the same. There are 5 caramels, 5 with peanut butter, and 3 mints; the rest are pure chocolate. What is the probability that you will choose a plain chocolate? State the probability or the missing information.

3 There are four different colors on a spinner. One of them is red. What is the probability that you will spin and get red? State the probability or the missing information.

4 Sketch a spinner that has the following probabilities:

One: $\frac{1}{8}$	Two: $\frac{1}{8}$	Three: $\frac{1}{4}$	Four: $\frac{1}{2}$

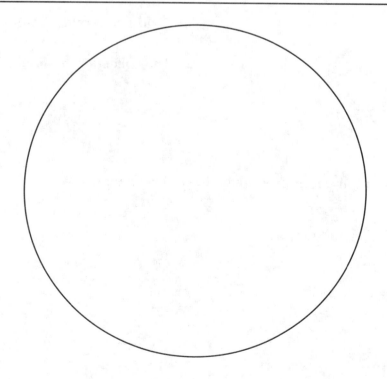

Probability and Statistics © 2005 Creative Teaching Press

Sample and Population
Introducing Statistics Vocabulary

Population: The entire group or set from which you *want* to gather data.
Sample: A random set of a population from which you *actually* gather data.

Look at the two examples below. In the first example, the sample is only a part of the population. In the second example, the sample and the population are the same.

Example 1
A group uses a computer program to randomly choose 100 people to call in a city of 12,600 people. The group calls and asks these people whom they will vote for in the next election. The group uses this information to predict which candidate will win the election.

Example 2
Mrs. Carson wants to know the average math score on the tests she just graded. She adds all the scores together and divides by the number of students in her class. She uses this information to decide if the class knows the information well enough to go on to the next math skill.

In the first example, the sample is the number of people called (100), and the population is the number of people in the entire city (12,600). The sample is certainly part of the population, but it is not the entire population. In the second example, Mrs. Carson has a much smaller population to study, so it makes sense for her to include all the test scores in the sample.

Read each example. Underline the phrase that tells what the person wants to know. Write *whole* **if the sample includes all of the population. Write** *part* **if it includes only part of the population.**

1 Natalie wants to know the average age at which a person can obtain a driver's license in the United States. She uses the Internet to check every state's motor vehicle laws. She records the information she finds and is able to use all of it in her study.

2 Camille thinks her father's gym could sell more memberships if it provided child care in the gym. To test her theory, she stands outside a grocery store for a few hours each day for a week and asks shoppers if they will answer a few questions. Some people agree to answer the questions, and she finds that most of these people agree they would be more likely to go to a gym if it had on-site day care.

3 Danny is writing a story for his creative-writing class, and one of the characters is a five-year-old boy. He wants the story to be realistic, so he asks his five-year-old brother to tell him what five-year-olds like to eat. He uses his brother's answer in the story.

So What?
Understanding How the Sample Affects the Answer

If the sample and the population of a study are the same, then the final answer is exact. If the sample is only part of the population, then the answer is an estimate. The bigger the difference between the sample and population, the more likely it is that the final answer could be inaccurate.

Think about it. Tomorrow the class is celebrating an upcoming holiday. You want to bring a special treat that the whole class will like to eat. Which will provide a more accurate idea of what everyone wants: asking the one student sitting next to you or asking half the class? Neither sample includes the entire class, but asking half the class will give you a more accurate estimate than asking just one person.

Read each situation. Write whether or not you think it is reasonable to trust the results. Then tell why. Be prepared to discuss your answers in class.

1 A man invents a diet pill. He goes to a local exercise class and convinces five women to take the pill. Four of the women are successful at losing at least a little weight. He publishes an advertisement that claims, "Four out of every five people who took my pill lost weight!" He sells a lot of pills.

Probability and Statistics © 2005 Creative Teaching Press

Continue to page 2.

So What?

2 A chewing gum company invents a gum that it believes will help prevent cavities. The company publishes an advertisement in a national dental journal that asks dentists to test the gum. The company gets 500 dentists to each give the gum to ten patients. At the end of the study, the gum company has 5,000 dental records. The company finds that the gum does not prevent cavities in the sample studied, but it does not seem to cause them either. (The sample gets the same number of cavities as non-gum-chewers do.) The company uses an advertising campaign that stresses that its gum does not cause cavities. Sales go up.

3 Carrie has to write a report for her sociology class. She hates to do library research, so instead she decides to do her own research. Her neighbor cares for two three-year-olds every afternoon. After watching the children for a week, Carrie writes a report on the typical vocabulary development of a three-year-old.

4 Raul has to write a report for his economics class. There are three gas stations in his town. He talks two out of three of the local gas station owners into letting him have the records of their gas prices every day for a year. He uses a computer program to average the gas prices in each season and writes a report titled "The Average Difference in Gas Prices by Season for Our Town."

Probability and Statistics © 2005 Creative Teaching Press

Stats and Facts
Introducing More Statistics Vocabulary

A **hypothesis** is an educated guess at an answer to a question. Statistical studies are often based on a hypothesis. For example, studies that look at how well a new medicine works are often trying to prove that it does work.

Data is the information you gather from your sample. Real-life statisticians have very strict rules about how to go about gathering data to make the study dependable.

Read each study. Answer the questions.

1 You keep hitting your head on the doorway of your science classroom. It seems unusually low. You want to find the average height of all the school doorways to convince the school to fix that door! There are 125 doorways. You measure the 15 doorways in the science wing.

What is the hypothesis?
What data are you collecting?
What is your population?
What is your sample?

2 You have to stoop low to use the school water fountains. You think it would benefit all students to have higher water fountains. You convince the school nurse to give you the individual heights of all the boys at your school—without any names attached.

What is the hypothesis?
What data are you collecting?
What is your population?
What is your sample?
Are your results likely to be more or less accurate than the ones in the first study? Why or why not?

3 Looking through the M&M's in your hand, you notice there do not seem to be as many brown ones as the other colors. You pour out all the M&M's in that bag to determine the number of brown candies compared to all the other colors of candies in the bag of M&M's.

What is the hypothesis?
What data are you collecting?
What is your population?
What is your sample?
Can you use this information to assume anything about all bags of M&M's candy? Why or why not?

Probability and Statistics © 2005 Creative Teaching Press

Finding "Normal"
Calculating Averages

The **average** is often considered "normal." That is what is implied when we hear *average height, average income,* or *average grade.* Finding the average is a key statistical skill.

An average is the outcome of adding all the values in a set of data and dividing by the number of values in that set.

Finding the Average

1 Gather the data. Make sure the units are all comparable. (That is, if you are measuring length, all units of measure must be standard or metric.) If they're not, convert them to a common system.

2 Find the sum of all the data in the set.

3 Divide the sum by the number of values in the data set. Be sure your answer includes the units of measure.

Example
Data: 3 cm, 6 cm, 12 cm
3 + 6 + 12 = 21
21 ÷ 3 = 7
The average of the data is 7 cm.

Find the average for each set of numbers.

1 8 cm, 5 cm, 4 cm, 5 cm, 3 cm

2 24, 15, 30

3 10°C, 20°C, 30°C, 50°C

4 4, 24, 16, 32

5 54, 72, 27

6 28', 56', 45', 67', 32', 45'

7 2, 5, 7, 4, 5, 3, 7, 8, 2, 4, 6, 7

8 3.6 in., 6.3 in., 6.0 in.

9 700, 1001, 898, 954, 1012, 987, 876, 568

10 4.5, 6.7, 5.5, 8.2, 4.1, 6.5, 3.5, 5.6, 7.7, 9.0

Convert Me
Finding Common Measurements

You think your little brother is watching too much television. You gather the following (
about his viewing habits for a week: 30 min., 1 hr., 45 min., 1.5 hr., 4 hr., 1.5 hr., and 5 hr

You want to find the average, but you have a problem: the measurements do not match.
Some of your data is in minutes, and some is in hours. You need to convert the data to a
common standard.

It is usually easier to convert to the smaller measurement. In this case, that is minutes.
Data: 30 min., 60 min., 45 min., 90 min., 240 min., 90 min., and 300 min.
Add: 30 + 60 + 45 + 90 + 240 + 90 + 300 = 855 min.
Divide: 855 min. ÷ 7 ≈ 122 min.
Your brother is watching television an average of 122 minutes, or about 2 hours, per day.

Find the average for each set of numbers. Convert to the smaller measurement.

1 1 in. = 2.54 cm   3 in., 5 in., 2 cm

2 1 kg = 2.2 lb.   70 lb., 35 kg, 78 lb., 36 kg

3 1 gal. = 3.8 L   6 gal., 16 L, 4 gal., 18 L

4 30%, $\frac{4}{10}$, 0.7, 0.8

5 $\frac{1}{3}$, $\frac{2}{3}$, $\frac{1}{3}$, $\frac{4}{6}$, $\frac{3}{6}$

6 0.6 in., 0.5 ft., 1.5 ft., 8 in., 6 in., 1.25 ft.

7 $\frac{1}{2}$, $\frac{3}{4}$, $\frac{2}{3}$, $\frac{5}{12}$

8 1 hr., 2 hr., 45 min., 12 min., 97 min.

Probability and Statistics © 2005 Creative Teaching Press

More Practice with Averages
Calculating Averages

Data: 4, 5, 6, 9, 7, 7

Average: $\dfrac{4+5+6+9+7+7}{6} = 6.\overline{33}$

Find the average for each set of numbers.

1 5, 5, 9, 8, 6, 8, 8

2 25, 32, 38, 56

3 1.5, 4.8, 2.6, 5.6, 4.3

4 980, 875, 365, 212

5 85, 25, 54, 34, 76, 77, 55

6 7.4, 8.45, 9, 6.22, 6.02

7 $0.42, $1.92, $0.84, $1.74, $2.02, $0.98

8 The low temperatures for five days were 12°, 5°, 18°, 16°, and 10°. What was the average low temperature?

9 The Cougars scored 65, 45, 34, 37, 36, 12, and 9 in seven games. What was the average score?

10 The total monthly rainfall for six months in Santa Rosa was 5.71", 11.65", 3.32", 1.52", 1.73", and 0.37". What was the average monthly rainfall during this period?

Fair Sample
Exploring Data Collection

When you use a sample of the population, you need to make sure it is **random,** or governed by chance.

Read each scenario. Answer the questions in complete sentences.

1 There are five math classes in your grade. One of the classes is an advanced class. All the classes are given the same timed multiplication test. Your principal wants to set a reasonable time in which students should complete the test. She tests the advanced class, records all the times of completion, and takes an average.

Do you think that the average completion time of the advanced math class will be similar to the time of all the other students in your grade? Explain.

If the principal takes the average of a different math class, is this a good random sample? How could it be better?

Probability and Statistics © 2005 Creative Teaching Press

Continue to page 2.

Fair Sample
Page 2

2 A new school has been built, and the administrators are worried there will not be enough funds for a good bus program. They want to convince voters to increase taxes to support more buses for the new school. As part of their research, they need to know the average number of miles a student at that school will travel from home to the school. They make a chart of some possible sample choices and the pros and cons of each.

Sample	Pro	Con
All students	Very accurate	Will take three weeks and two full-time employees to assemble, calculate, and check the data
All fourth-grade students	Reasonable sample size	Less accurate
All students with a last name beginning with *A*	Across grade levels	Less accurate

Tell which sample you would recommend to the administration and why.

Probability and Statistics © 2005 Creative Teaching Press

Finding Facts
Exploring Data Collection

Remember: Two key ways to get reliable results are to use a sample that is large *and* random.

There can be good reasons for choosing a particular sample, but that doesn't necessarily mean the sample is reliable.

Read each scenario. Answer the questions in complete sentences.

1 Joe wants to find the average percent of the population that speaks Spanish at home in the United States. He decides to use his hometown in Iowa as the sample. He uses data from the last census and finds the average. Why might that give an inaccurate result?

2 A meteorologist wants to determine the average temperature in January for the United States. She decides to use Florida's temperatures for each day of the month in January as the sample of the entire country, and she averages them. What is wrong with this approach?

3 You want to determine the average age of the people in your city. You decide to use your school as a sample. What is wrong with this scenario?

4 A clothing company wants to make more clothing in the most common sizes sold to teens. A data collection company sells them the size information from all the students at Greenwood Academy. What the company does not know is that Greenwood Academy is a sumo wrestling school on Greenwood Street. How might this cause problems for the company?

5 Matt cannot stand the plain white walls at his workplace for one more day. He feels certain that morale and productivity at the company will improve if he can convince his bosses to hang art with bright, vibrant colors on the wall. He avoids the large group of workers he does not know very well and polls only the five workers who already know him well and consider him a friend. How is he making multiple mistakes?

Probability and Statistics © 2005 Creative Teaching Press

Next Step
Finding the Range

> **Range:** The difference between the greatest and least measurement of the data set.
>
> **Range = Greatest Value – Least Value**
>
> **Example**
> **Test scores:** 80%, 85%, 62%, 99%, 100%, 77%, 70%, 99%, 89%, 92%
> 100 – 62 = 38. The range is 38.

Find the range.

1 82, 65, 54, 76, 54, 19

2 6, 7, 8, 2, 4, 6, 12, 5, 2, 5, 7, 9, 1

3 78, 67, 54, 36, 87, 85, 92, 59, 60, 100, 78, 76, 45, 78, 85, 92

4 2,700; 13,001; 1,898; 9,541; 12,012; 1,987; 8,716; 5,167

5 14.5, 6.71, 15.32, 8.2, 14.1, 6.5, 13.15, 15.26, 7.7, 9.0

6 $\frac{5}{12}, \frac{11}{12}, \frac{3}{12}, \frac{7}{12}, \frac{1}{12}, \frac{9}{12}$

7 $3.95, $2.21, $8.23, $1.75, $5.57, $5.49, $2.85, $1.97

8 7.05, 5.78, 3.09, 12.8, 4.92, 7.65, 8, 10.54

9 $\frac{1}{5}, \frac{3}{8}, \frac{2}{5}, \frac{1}{ }, \frac{3}{ }, \frac{2}{3}, \frac{4}{5}, \frac{7}{8}, \frac{2}{5}$

10 What _____ of the range says about the data? Explain.

Great Range
Practicing Range Calculation

Range = Greatest Value – Least Value

Calculate to find the range.

1 A group of children is taking an archery class. On the last day, they have a competition. The farthest arrow flies 75 feet. One arrow travels only 16 feet. What is the range between the two distances?

2 Students in Mrs. Green's class wrote essays for a citywide contest. The shortest essay was 375 words long. The longest essay was 1,254 words long. What was the range of the word count?

3 Melissa is helping out at her father's veterinary clinic. It is her job to weigh the animals every morning to watch for sudden changes in weight. Today her smallest animal is a lizard that weighs only 9 ounces. The largest animal is a mixed-breed dog that weighs 78 pounds, 7 ounces. What is the range in animal weights at the clinic this morning?

4 Kyra is collecting data for a report on local rainfall. She assembles the averages in a graph. The month with the least amount of rain for the region is July, when only 0.25 inch of rain was recorded. This contrasts sharply with the dampest month, February, in which 12.56 inches of rain fell. What is the range in rainfall for the area?

5 Henry is the assistant swim coach at the high school. It is his job to track the times of the junior varsity boys swimmers. Today his slowest swimmer completed the sprint in 42 seconds. His fastest swimmer completed the sprint in 29 seconds. What is the range in swimming times?

6 Austin is tracking the growth of 20 tomato seedlings for his science fair experiment. His smallest seedling is only 3 centimeters tall. His tallest seedling is already half a meter tall! What is the range?

Probability and Statistics © 2005 Creative Teaching Press

Greater Range
Finding Average and Range

Average = $\dfrac{\text{sum of data}}{\text{number of data scores}}$

Range = Greatest Value – Least Value

Compute the average and range. Use complete sentences to describe your findings. Round to the nearest tenth as needed.

1 The number of students in each science class in the school
Data: 29, 30, 25, 32, 28, 30

2 The number of hours worked each day in a week
Data: 7, 5, 8, 10, 6, 8, 3

3 The number of students at each bus stop
Data: 1, 5, 10, 3, 6, 9, 4, 6, 7, 8, 5, 2, 1, 7, 8, 9

4 The length of time it takes each student in a class to get ready for school
Data: 30 min., 45 min., 1 hr., 1.5 hr., 40 min., 1 hr., 2 hr., 1.25 hr., 1.75 hr., 50 min., 20 min., 25 min., 35 min., 1 hr., 30 min., 45 min., 20 min., 40 min., 1 hr., 30 min., 25 min., 35 min., 70 min., 1 hr., 30 min., 20 min., 25 min.

5 The length of each phone call on Monday
Data: 9 min., 50 sec., 5 min., 1 hr. and 5 min., 22 sec., 55 min., 17 min., 6 min., 3 min., 49 sec.

Personal Averages
Exploring Real-Life Statistics

Use the chart to record your data. Then calculate the average for each activity at the end of the week.

	Total Time Spent Sleeping	Total Time Spent Doing Homework	Total Time Spent Watching TV	Total Time Spent Talking on Phone
Tuesday				
Wednesday				
Thursday				
Friday				
Saturday				
Sunday				
Weekly Average				

Probability and Statistics © 2005 Creative Teaching Press

This 'n' That

Review

Solve.

1 Find the average and range. (1 kg = 2.2 lb.)
Data: 40 lb., 20 kg, 44 lb., 23 kg

2 Find the average and range for the number of adults in each motorcycle safety course this summer.
Data: 18, 22, 17, 24, 18, 20, 18, 19, 24

3 A controversial show comes to town. You are writing a story about the issues that surround the show for your school paper. You want to know the percentage of high-school students planning to see the show, so you poll everyone in Mr. Johnson's freshman English class. Why won't this method cover your population properly? What sample might provide more accurate results?

4 Explain the difference between sample and population. When might they be the same?

Continue to page 2.

5 **Data:** 15°C, 74°F, 22°C, 90°F, 18°C, 77°F, 90°F, 88°F, 45°F
What do you have to do before you can make any calculations with this data?

6 A pharmaceutical company develops a new heart medicine. They test it on 2,000 adult males and find that it works and is safe for this population. When the medicine is approved for use throughout the United States, it is prescribed to adult men and women with heart problems. Where is the flaw in this experiment?

7 Find the average and range for the number of aphids found on each diseased rosebush in the garden.
Data: 88, 92, 75, 82, 78, 90, 78, 79, 94

8 Find the average and range for the cost of a triple mocha at each coffee shop in the city.
Data: $3.95, $2.95, $3.50, $3.75, $3.95, $3.25, $3.50, $3.95

Probability and Statistics © 2005 Creative Teaching Press

Put It in Order
Organizing Data

Data is easier to work with when it is organized. You can list numbers from greatest to least or least to greatest. You can put dates in chronological order. You can put words in alphabetical order.

No   **Data:** 2, 10, 7, 6, 4, 2

Yes   **Data:** 2, 2, 4, 6, 7, 10 **OR** 10, 7, 6, 4, 2, 2

Tell how you would organize each set of data.

1 Quiz scores: 10 pts., 9 pts., 7 pts., 8 pts., 10 pts., 8 pts., 7 pts., 6 pts.

2 The days worked each month: Sept. 20, Aug. 19, Jan. 22, Dec. 12, Mar. 18, May 24, July 15, June 21, Feb. 22, Apr. 25, Oct. 19, Nov. 23

3 The percentage of bacteria growth: 78, 67, 54, 36, 87, 85, 92, 59, 60, 100, 78, 76, 45, 78, 85, 92

4 The purchased fraction of the total tickets available: $\frac{1}{5}, \frac{3}{8}, \frac{2}{5}, \frac{1}{2}, \frac{3}{4}, \frac{2}{3}, \frac{4}{5}, \frac{7}{8}, \frac{2}{5}$

5 The price of a product at local retailers: $0.42, $1.92, $0.84, $1.73, $2.02, $0.98

6 The distance of a first jump:

$60\frac{1}{5}", 58\frac{3}{8}", 43\frac{2}{5}", 61\frac{1}{2}", 47\frac{3}{4}", 72\frac{2}{3}", 60\frac{4}{5}", 61\frac{7}{8}", 60\frac{2}{5}"$

The Three Ms
Finding the Mean, Median, and Mode

Mean: the average
Median: the middle value of the data set when the data is arranged in order from least to greatest or greatest to least. (If there are two middle numbers, you take the average of the two numbers.)
Mode: the data value that appears most frequently. There may be more than one mode in a data set. If the most common values appear three times, then each of those values is a mode. If each value is used only once, all of the values are modes.

Data: 1, 2, 3, 4, 5, 6, 6, 7, 8, 8, 9, 10
The **mean** is 5.75.   The **median** is 6.   The **modes** are 6 and 8.

Organize each set of data, and state the mean, median, and mode.

1 Test scores: 88%, 93%, 76%, 54%, 98%, 65%, 100%, 98%, 63%, 56%

Mean:
Median:
Mode(s):

2 Times to run a mile: 10 min., 15 min., 12 min., 14 min., 12 min., 17 min., 11 min.

Mean:
Median:
Mode(s):

Continue to page 2.

The Three Ms

3 The number of touchdowns in each football game during the season: 5, 6, 7, 3, 2, 5, 6, 7, 8, 6

Mean:
Median:
Mode(s):

4 The time spent playing video games each day: 30 min., 1 hr., 1.5 hr., 45 min., 15 min., 30 min., 40 min.

Mean:
Median:
Mode(s):

5 Teachers like to see the mean, median, and modes of test scores close to one another. What does it say about the data if those values are within a close range? What could cause data to be within a close range compared to a large range? Consider the following sets of data as examples:

Class A test scores—70, 75, 78, 80, 85, 85, 90, 95, 100
Class B test scores—12, 22, 33, 85, 90, 95, 95, 95, 100

Answer in complete sentences.

Probability and Statistics © 2005 Creative Teaching Press

Mmmm
Finding the Mean, Median, and Mode

> **Mean:** the average
> **Median:** the middle value of the data set when the data is arranged in order
> **Mode:** the data value that appears most frequently

Find the mean, median, and mode for each set of data.

1 6, 9, 8, 9, 12, 15, 12, 6, 9, 7, 15, 12

2 0.43, 0.76, 0.46, 0.55, 0.25, 0.32, 0.37, 0.50

3 $3\frac{4}{5}"$, $4\frac{3}{5}"$, $3\frac{7}{8}"$, $2\frac{5}{8}"$, $2\frac{7}{8}"$

4 16, 23, 18, 30, 19, 37, 23, 30, 33, 16, 30

5 17,423; 13,678; 19,555; 18,000; 16,894

6 $24.00, $160.00, $78.00, $44.00, $48.00, $36.00, $44.00

Probability and Statistics © 2005 Creative Teaching Press

The Parade
Problem Solving with Mean, Median, and Mode

The sun is shining brightly. It's time for the Butter and Eggs Day Parade! Helen is busy taking information from each group in the parade. Use Helen's chart to answer the questions on the next page.

Group	No. of People Riding on Float	No. of Animals Participating	Approx. Weight of Float	Throwing Candy?
4-H	8	24	1.50 tons	yes
Larson's Drug	4	0	1.75 tons	yes
ABC Day Care	12	2	1.50 tons	yes
Central High Marching Band	6 (56 marching)	2	2.25 tons	no
Bob's Feed and Grain	8	2	3.00 tons	yes
Girl Scouts	24	4	1.50 tons	yes
Boy Scouts	18	0	1.50 tons	yes
Central Farm Co-Op	6	2	2.25 tons	yes
Acme Hardware	4	1	2.00 tons	no

Continue to page 2.

The Parade
Page 2

Solve.

1 Helen wants to arrange the floats so that the smallest floats are at the front and the largest are at the back. Assume that the weight of the float and the number of people riding indicates its relative size. How would you order the floats?

2 The judges ask Helen to tell them the average number of animals participating. She thinks they really want to know the most common number of animals on the floats. Calculate the average; then calculate the mode. Then write a sentence telling why Helen thinks the mode will be more useful than the mean.

3 The parade committee has to pay a special tax to the city if the average weight of the floats is over 2 tons. Will they have to pay the tax this year?

4 What is the range for the number of people riding on the floats? (Do not include the 56 members of the marching band; only include the 6 members of the homecoming court riding with them.)

Probability and Statistics © 2005 Creative Teaching Press

Name _____ Date _____

The Bars Show and Tell
Understanding Bar Graphs

Use this chart to help you answer the questions on the next page.

Average Hours of Homework for Seventh Graders by Day

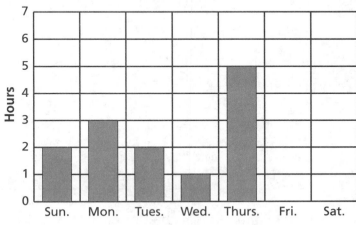

Question	Answer
What was the original question?	Look at the title, any key or legend, and any other labels. For this graph, the question appears to have been, "How many hours of homework do you have each night?"
What is the population?	If the title does not tell you, the graph does not have enough information to be very reliable. Often a test question or math book will use fictitious data, and in that case, you won't find population information. For example, it might say "Average Rainfall" but not tell you for which location.
How big is the sample?	Depending on the way the graph is set up, you might be able to total the numbers in all columns. However, you can't always get this information directly from the graph.

The Bars Show and Tell

Page 2

1 According to the data, which nights of the week were students least likely to spend doing homework?

3 Can you tell the sample size of this data?

2 Which night seems to involve the most homework?

4 What is the population?

Female Population in the United States, 1997

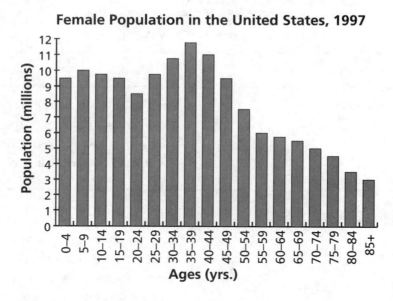

5 In 1997, the greatest number of women were in which age range?

7 What is the range of ages?

6 How old would those women be today?

Probability and Statistics © 2005 Creative Teaching Press

Name _____   Date _____

Money!
Reading Bar Graphs

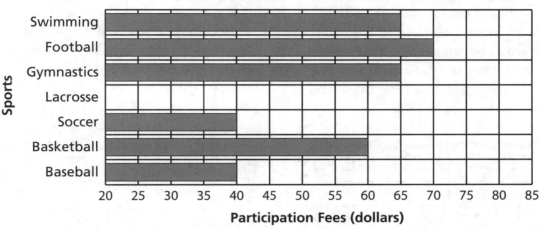

Average Participation Fees by Sport at Central High

Sports (y-axis): Swimming, Football, Gymnastics, Lacrosse, Soccer, Basketball, Baseball

Participation Fees (dollars) (x-axis): 20 25 30 35 40 45 50 55 60 65 70 75 80 85

Use the graph to answer the questions.

1 What is the population of the study?

2 You investigate, and it turns out that all the data came from the coaches of the boys' teams. All the coaches of the girls' teams are away this week at a conference, so you can't verify that they have the same fees. How could you retitle the graph to more accurately reflect the population?

3 Which sport has the highest participation fee? How much is it?

4 Which sport has the lowest participation fee? How much is it?

5 What is the average participation fee at Central High?

6 There are two modes in this data set. What are they, and what sports do they represent?

7 What is the median participation fee?

8 How much would it cost to participate in soccer, swimming, and lacrosse?

9 What is the difference in participation fees for swimming and soccer?

10 If your parents had budgeted $60 for you for participation fees, which sports could you play?

Graph Ranges
Using the Range to Begin Graphing

One way to plot data is to start with a baseline of 0 and have the top line of your graph be equal to *or a little more than* the greatest data value. This works well when the range is not too great and when one of your values is 0.

If none of your values is 0, assign the smallest data value to the bottom line, and have the top line of your graph be equal to *or a little more than* the greatest data value.

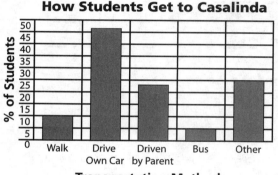

How Students Get to Casalinda

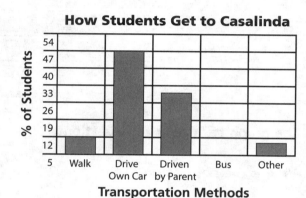

How Students Get to Casalinda

If the data is a mix of whole and decimal values, use whole numbers on the graph, and round up to the next whole number for the top line.

Read the data. Fill in the first and last data values for each set of data.

1 6, 4, 8, 9, 12, 15, 12, 6, 9, 7, 15, 12, 0, 0, 4

2 0.43, 0.76, 0.46, 0.55, 0.25, 0.31, 0.37, 0.50

Continue to page 2.

Graph Ranges
Page 2

3 9, 11, 0, 13, 3, 7, 15, 5, 7, 21, 18, 29

_____

4 6, 23, 18, 30, 19, 37, 23, 30, 33, 17, 30

_____

5 17,423; 13,678; 19,554; 18,000; 16,894

_____

6 $24.00, $160.00, $80.00, $44.00, $48.00, $36.00, $44.00

_____

7 75°, 77°, 83°, 85°, 83°, 87°, 92°, 89°, 81°, 83°

_____

8 1.5, 3, 8, 11, 15, 20, 25

_____

Probability and Statistics © 2005 Creative Teaching Press

Label It
Understanding the Importance of Graph Labels

Give the reader as much information as possible about your population, sample, and experiment by labeling the graph well.

Henry polls two English classes at each grade level of Casalinda High School in order to see which religious faiths are represented at the school. The population is students at Casalinda, the sample is English students at each grade level, and the data reflects religious faiths.

Religious Faiths Represented at Casalinda

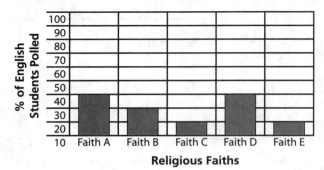

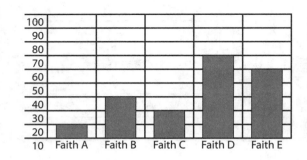

Which graph gives the reader more information?

Use the information provided to label each graph. Do not include specific data numbers or individual column titles for this exercise.

1 A study of the Casalinda High School swim team reveals the students' favorite breakfast foods. The population is all high-school swimmers, the sample is high-school swimmers at Casalinda High School, and the data reflects their favorite breakfast foods.

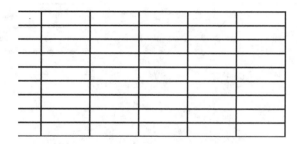

Probability and Statistics © 2005 Creative Teaching Press

Continue to page 2.

Label It
Page 2

2 A study of the Casalinda High School choir investigates the students' reasons for joining the choir. The population is Casalinda choir members, the sample is Casalinda choir members, and the data reflects their reasons for joining the choir.

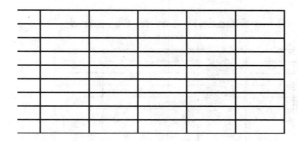

3 A study of Casalinda High School students investigates how students get to school. The population is all Casalinda students, the sample is a random survey sent through the mail to 20 percent of the student body, and the data reflects transportation methods used to get to school.

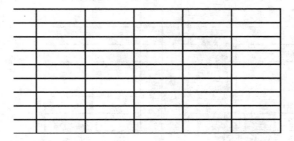

Probability and Statistics © 2005 Creative Teaching Press

Choose an Increment
Practicing Graphing Skills

Once your graph has the greatest and least data values, you need to decide on the increments in between. If your first value is 0, divide the greatest value by the number of lines you want to have on your graph to get your increment. For this graph, the greatest value was less than 50 percent, but ten lines made an easy-to-read graph; so 50 percent was chosen as the top value, and increments of 5 percent were used.

How Students Get to Casalinda

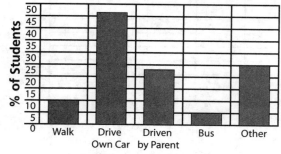

Transportation Methods

If the first line is your least data value, then find the range of your data values, and divide that by the number of lines you want to have. That is your increment value. If it's an awkward number, you can adjust the value of your final line up to make a range that divides evenly.

How Students Get to Casalinda

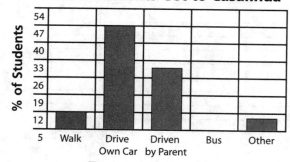

Transportation Methods

Probability and Statistics © 2005 Creative Teaching Press

Continue to page 2.

Choose an Increment

Page 2

Use the information on the previous page to help you decide on an increment, and then label the graph.

1 First Semester Student Absences
Population and Sample: Students in Room 12
September: 8
October: 18
November: 22
December: 16
January: 22

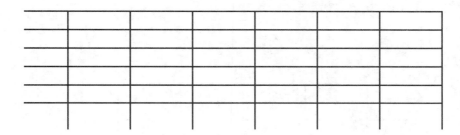

2 Children in Permanent Residence
Population and Sample: Children living in the Westside housing development
Indian Creek Circle: 15
Desert Drive: 42
Flying Arrow Court: 18
Pontiac Place: 35
Mustang Street: 32

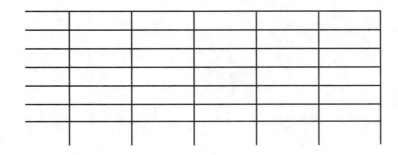

Probability and Statistics © 2005 Creative Teaching Press

Name _____ Date _____

Creating a Bar Graph
Practicing Graphing Skills

---

1 Determine the range of the data. Use this to set up and label the rows of your graph.

2 Determine the categories for your bars. Use this to set up your columns and label each category.

3 Label the graph.

Graph each set of data.

1 Enrollment for City Parks and Recreation Courses, Spring (by number of people): Weaving, 8; Tap Dance, 12; Painting, 8; Aerobics, 48; Knitting, 6

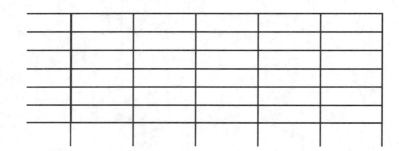

2 Favorite School Lunches (by percent): Pizza, 40; American Chop Suey, 12; Spaghetti, 13; Grilled Cheese, 6; Hot Dog and Soda, 17; Chicken Bites, 12

Probability and Statistics © 2005 Creative Teaching Press

Continue to page 2.

Creating a Bar Graph
Page 2

3 Fruit Production (in bushels): Lemon, 600; Lime, 450; Orange, 1,400

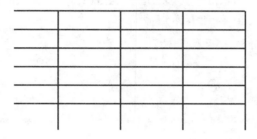

4 Dog Breeds in Neighborhood (by number of dogs): Golden Retriever, 8; Labrador, 11; Poodle, 2; Terrier, 3; Beagle, 7

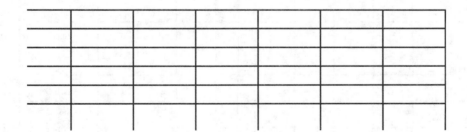

Probability and Statistics © 2005 Creative Teaching Press

Real-Life Graphing I
Plotting Data on a Bar Graph

Favorites transfer well to bar graphs. Use the following steps to gather and plot your data.

1 Pick a specific population to poll, such as people of a certain age, gender, or location.

2 Decide how you are going to gather accurate and fair data for that population. (In other words, identify a reasonable sample.)

3 Poll the sample, and record your data.

4 Plot the data in a graph.

5 Label the graph clearly.

Record your data on lined paper. Use the grid below to create your graph.

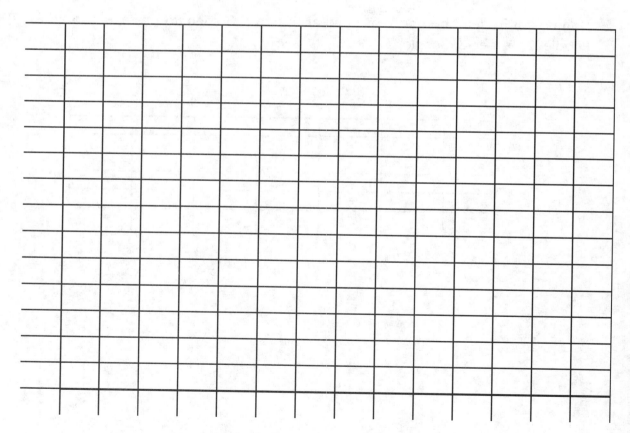

Name _____ Date _____

I See Dots
Understanding Scatter Plots

A **scatter plot** is a graph of two related sets of data on an XY axis.

A **linear correlation** is a scatter plot that forms a "line" showing that one axis seems to depend on or relate to the other.

Scatter plots are useful when you want to study related pairs, such as height vs. weight. A graph may show linear correlation. If a graph has a linear correlation, then the properties of the data relate. If there is no linear correlation, the properties are not related.

1.
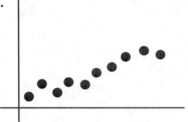

2.
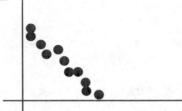

3.
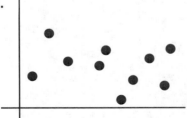

4.
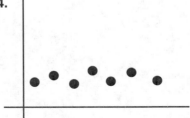

The first two examples show linear correlation. You can't draw a perfectly straight line in Examples 1 and 2. However, you can see a line shape. In Example 1, the correlation is that the higher the value on the X-axis, the higher the value on the Y-axis. In Example 2, the correlation is that the higher the value on the X-axis, the lower the value on the Y-axis. The third and fourth examples show no correlation. In Example 3, the dots seem random. In Example 4, it looks like you could draw a straight line. However, the placement of the Y-value does not seem to change dependent on the X-value. Because the X-value does not relate to the Y-value, there is no correlation. To have linear correlation, the line cannot be vertical or horizontal.

Probability and Statistics © 2005 Creative Teaching Press

Continue to page 2.

I See Dots
Page 2

Examine the graphs. Tell if you think there is linear correlation. If there is, explain the correlation.

 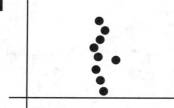

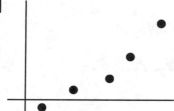

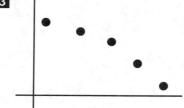

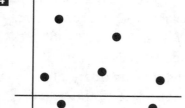

Probability and Statistics © 2005 Creative Teaching Press

Plotting Points
Graphing Scatter Plots

A scatter plot is only for pairs of related data. Assign one data set as the X-values and one data set as the Y-values. Then plot as you normally would on an XY axis.

Height (in.)	Weight (lb.)
32	20
38	40
45	45
48	55
53	70
56	90

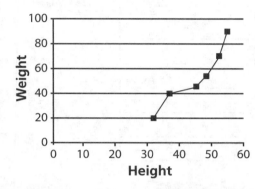

Read each set of data. Plot the points. Then make a scatter plot to display the data.

Puppy Growth

1

Height (in.)	Weight (lb.)
6	1.5
8	3
9.5	8
12	11
13	15
15	20
18	25

Weed Growth

2

No. of Weeds in 8 sq. ft.	Rain (in.) in Previous Week
6	0.02
7	0.09
9	0.11
14	0.52
20	0.66
45	0.78
49	0.23

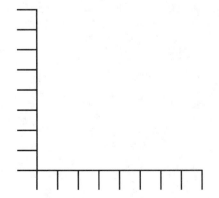

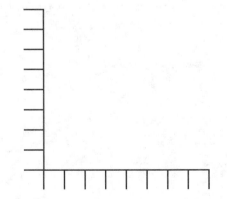

Continue to page 2.

Plotting Points
Page 2

3 Age by Grade

Age	Grade
5	K
6	1
8	2
7	2
9	4
7	1
10	5

4 Age by Number of Siblings

Age	No. of Siblings
9	0
10	1
7	2
6	0
9	1
5	5
7	3

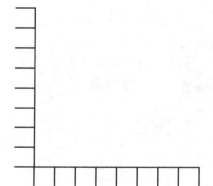

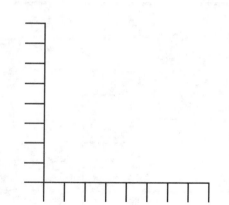

5 Which graph above shows the least amount of correlation between the two data sets?

Probability and Statistics © 2005 Creative Teaching Press

Name _____ Date _____

A Good Plot
Creating More Scatter Plots

Remember: Assign one data set as the X-values and one data set as the Y-values. Then plot as you normally would on an XY axis.

Read each set of data. Plot the points.

1 Spelling Test

Hours of TV Watched in a Week	Spelling Test Score
2	100
4	90
10	70
8	75
2	95
0	100
4	85
8	80
7	70
9	65

2 Reading and Height

Words per Minute	Height (in.)
125	60
105	55
132	52
159	50
123	63
181	63
110	69
125	72
129	58
133	56

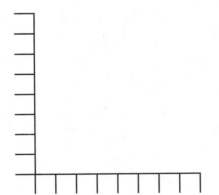

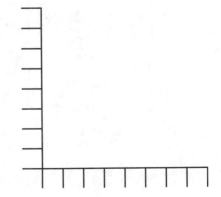

Continue to page 2.

A Good Plot

Page 2

3 **Number of Pages and Price of Fiction Novels**

No. of Pages	Paperback Price
150	$5.95
105	$4.95
183	$5.95
210	$8.95
255	$12.95
192	$5.95
221	$8.95
270	$12.95
450	$19.95
249	$8.95

4 **Number of Kids at Playground**

Time of Day (by 24 hrs.)	Kids at Playground
6:00	0
8:00	0
10:00	2
12:00	12
14:00	10
16:00	6
18:00	0
20:00	2
22:00	0
24:00	0

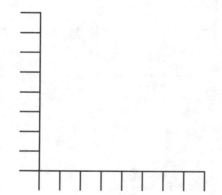

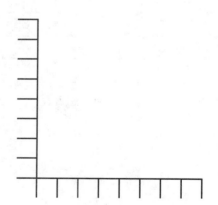

5 Which graph above shows the least amount of correlation between the two data sets?

Probability and Statistics © 2005 Creative Teaching Press

More Dots
Practicing with Scatter Plots

Hours Studied	Grade on Test	Hours Studied	Grade on Test
2	76	1.25	55
2.25	82	5	100
0	45	6	100
1	50	4	98
2	69	3	90
3	85	3.75	95
4	90	0.5	40

Display the data using a scatter plot. Determine if there is a correlation. If there is a correlation, describe it, and tell how you could use one piece of data to predict the other. If you do not see a correlation, write a paragraph explaining why you believe there is no correlation.

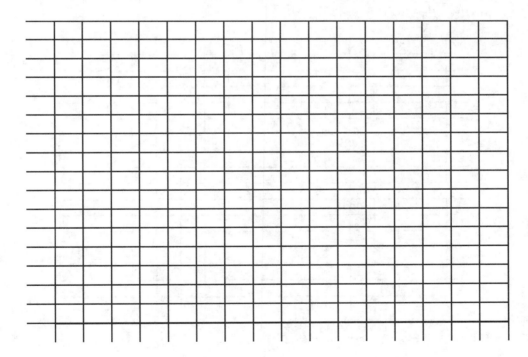

_____

_____

_____

_____

Real-Life Graphing II
Practicing with Scatter Plots

Measure the height and arm span of twelve classmates. The arm span is the length from finger-tip to fingertip when the arms are completely outstretched. Record your data in either inches or centimeters.

Height	Arm Span		Height	Arm Span

Make a scatter plot to display the data.

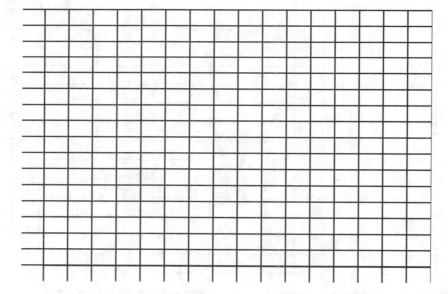

Answer the questions based on your scatter plot.

1 Do you think that there is a linear correlation between height and arm span?

2 If given one of the values, do you think that you could predict the other value?

Probability and Statistics © 2005 Creative Teaching Press

Show Me
Review

Remember: Regardless of the type of graph, it can be helpful to put the data in order before you begin.

Read the data. Find the mean, median, and mode. On the next page, plot one set of data as a bar graph. Choose two sets of data to plot as a scatter plot. Use labels to show clearly which data you used.

Zoo Lizard

Age	Length	Weight
Hatchling	5 in.	2 oz.
2 mo.	8 in.	4 oz.
4 mo.	10 in.	8 oz.
6 mo.	12 in.	10 oz.
8 mo.	12.5 in.	12 oz.
10 mo.	13 in.	12 oz.
1 yr.	14 in.	13 oz.
14 mo.	15 in.	15 oz.
16 mo.	16 in.	1 lb.
18 mo.	18 in.	1 lb., 4 oz.

Continue to page 2.

Show Me
Page 2

Use the data on the previous page to create a bar graph and a scatter plot.

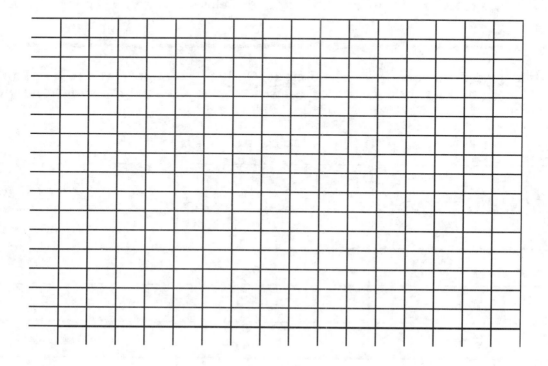

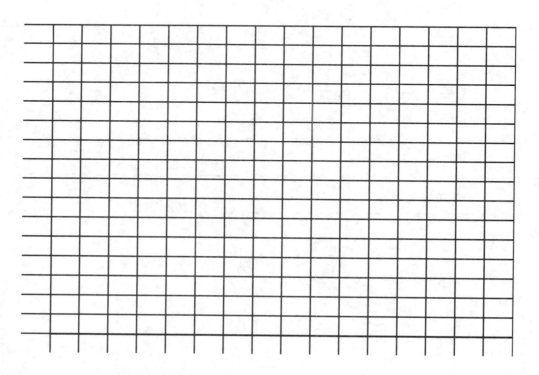

Probability and Statistics © 2005 Creative Teaching Press

Name _____   Date _____

Pie in the Sky
Reading Pie Graphs

Pie graphs show parts of a whole. They are especially useful for showing percents visually. They are not useful for showing changes over time, and you can only compare two pie graphs to each other when they each represent the same whole. A good pie graph actually includes the percentage next to or inside of the "pie slice," but if that information is not included, you can estimate the percentage by estimating the fraction of the circle that the slice occupies and converting that to a percent.

Read the graph, and answer the questions.

1  **Popular Dogs**

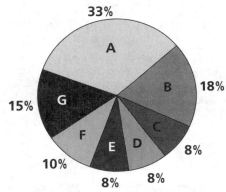

A Labrador Retriever E Yorkshire Terrier
B Golden Retriever   F German Shepherd
C Beagle   G Other
D Schnauzer

a. Which dog is the most popular?

b. How much more popular is it than the next most popular dog?

c. Which single dog was listed as the least popular?

d. Can it be assumed that this dog is still more popular than any of the dogs included in "Other"?

e. The popularity of the beagle equals that of which two other dogs?

2 **Ethnicity of U.S. Public School Students**

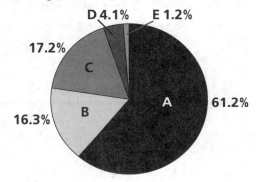

A White, Non-Hispanic
B Hispanic
C Black, Non-Hispanic
D Asian/Pacific Islander
E American Indian/Alaskan

a. There are about as many black, non-Hispanic students as there are _____ students.

b. What is the range for this data?

c. The ethnicity with the smallest representation among U.S. public school students is _____.

d. The white, non-Hispanic percentage is very close to what fraction of the pie?

Probability and Statistics © 2005 Creative Teaching Press

Pies and Percents
Building Pie Graphs from Decimals

If the data is still raw, find the percentage by setting up a ratio of the part to the whole and calculating the decimal. Then turn that number into a percent.

Cars in the School Parking Lot

Make of Car	No. in Parking Lot	% of Whole
Chevy	35	27
Toyota	27	20
Ford	32	24
Kia	15	11
Honda	23	17

The percent for Chevy was found by summing the data to find the whole and dividing the number for that category by the whole.

$$\text{Chevy} = \frac{35}{132} = 0.6\overline{51} \approx 27\%$$

Find the percent for each piece of raw data.

1   **Favorite Sports**

Sport	No. of People	% of Whole
Swiming	6	
Football	18	
Soccer	12	
Baseball	2	
Basketball	4	

2   **Points Earned This Weekend**

Team	Points Earned	% of Whole
San Francisco	16	
Los Angeles	22	
Chicago	28	
Phoenix	31	
Baltimore	15	

Probability and Statistics © 2005 Creative Teaching Press

Continue to page 2.

Pies and Percents
Page 2

3

Hours Spent Cleaning This Week

Room in House	Hrs. Spent Cleaning	% of Whole
Bedroom	11	
Dining Room	2	
Kitchen	7	
Living Room	2	
Library	1	

4

Canadian Elections, 2000

Party	No. of Seats	% of Whole
Liberal	172	
Bloc Québécois	38	
Reform/Cdn. Alliance	67	
New Democratic Party	12	
Progressive Conservative	12	
Independent	0	

5

Share of Peltville County Cheese Market

Seller	Units Sold	% of Whole
Big Mart	580	
Joe's Market	212	
Henrietta's Cheese Mkt.	1562	
Cheese R Us	1812	
Cheese World	5521	

Decimal Pie
Creating Pie Graphs

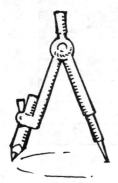

To make an exact pie graph, use a compass to draw a circle. Change the percent to a decimal, and multiply it by the total degrees in a circle.

Vanilla	15	22%

$$0.22 \times 360° \approx 79.2°$$

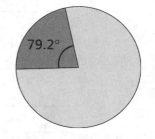

79.2°

That is the angle of your pie wedge. Draw a line of radius, and use your protractor to find where the second radius should intersect the circle to create the correct pie wedge for that data.

Use the data to complete the chart. Then graph the information in the pie graph.

Favorite Ice Cream

Flavor	No. of People Who Named the Flavor	% of Whole
Vanilla	15	
Chocolate	22	
Strawberry	10	
Neopolitan	6	
Other	15	

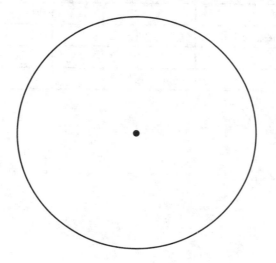

Probability and Statistics © 2005 Creative Teaching Press

More Pie Graphs
Creating Pie Graphs

Remember: Find the degrees of your pie wedge by multiplying the percentage of the circle by 360°.

Mountain	15	29%

$$0.29 \times 360° \approx 104.4°$$

Use the data to create a pie graph.

Bikes Sold This Week

Model	No. Sold	% of Whole
White Lightning	20	
Silver Streak	12	
Red Range	4	
Mountain	15	

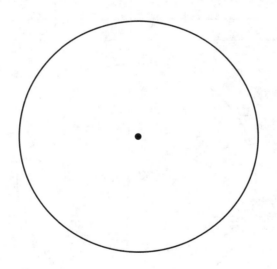

Apple Pie
Creating Pie Graphs

Remember: Find the degrees of your pie wedge by multiplying the percentage of the circle by 360°.

McIntosh	70	7.7%

$$0.077 \times 360° \approx 28°$$

Use the data to create a pie graph.

Apples Sold

Type	No. Sold	% of Whole
Red Delicious	200	
Golden Delicious	350	
Granny Smith	175	
Jonathan	50	
Winesap	55	
McIntosh	70	

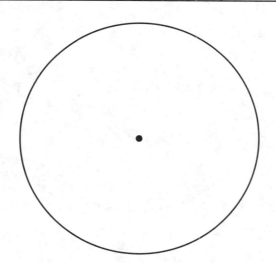

Probability and Statistics © 2005 Creative Teaching Press

Name _____   Date _____

Pumpkin Pie
Creating Pie Graphs

Remember: Find the degrees of your pie wedge by multiplying the percentage of the circle by 360°.

Howden Field	15	3%

$$0.03 \times 360° \approx 11°$$

Use the data to create a pie graph.

Pumpkins Sold

Type	No. Sold	% of Whole
Aspen	14	
Harvest Moon	62	
Jack-o'-Lantern	267	
Happy Jack	25	
Cinderella	150	
Chelsey	8	
Howden Field	15	

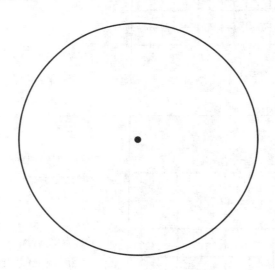

Probability and Statistics © 2005 Creative Teaching Press

Name _____   Date _____

Line Graphs!
Reading Line Graphs

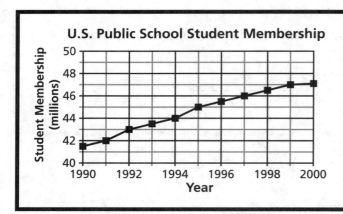

U.S. Public School Student Membership

Line graphs are useful for showing how something changes over time. Like scatter plots, they have an X-axis and a Y-axis. The X-axis typically shows time, and the Y-axis typically shows the numbers that correlate to the data.

Read the graphs and answer the questions.

1

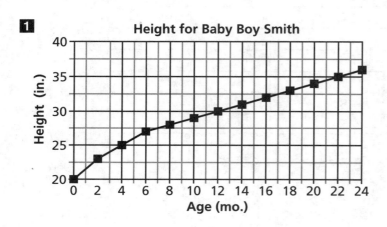

Height for Baby Boy Smith

What was Baby Boy Smith's height when he was 10 months old?

How much had he grown since his previous measurement?

How much did he grow altogether over the 2 years?

2

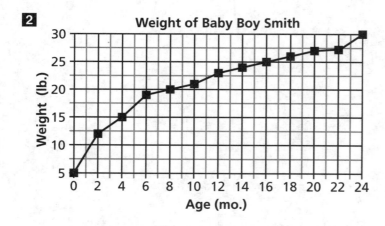

Weight of Baby Boy Smith

During which interval was there the greatest amount of weight gain?

During which interval was there the least change in Baby Boy Smith's weight?

How much weight did Baby Boy Smith gain over the 2 years charted?

Continue to page 2.

Line Graphs!
Page 2

3

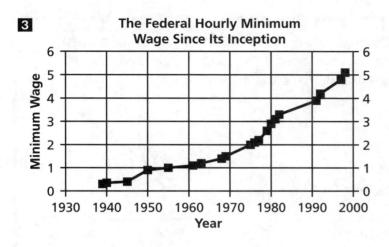

The Federal Hourly Minimum Wage Since Its Inception

What does this graph describe?

Was there ever a period when the minimum wage decreased?

What key piece of information is missing from one of the labels?

4

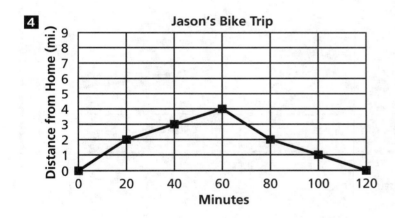

Jason's Bike Trip

How long did Jason's bike trip last?

There is a long hill somewhere during Jason's ride. During which period was he riding up it, and during which period was he riding down it?

5

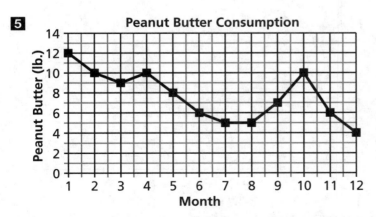

Peanut Butter Consumption

Is this likely a record of consumption by a home or a large cafeteria? Explain.

Each month is represented by its number. For which season of the year was the least peanut butter consumption recorded?

During which month were the fewest pounds of peanut butter consumed? Why do you think that was?

Trends
Reading Line Graphs

Line graphs are useful for seeing trends—changes that occur over time in a pattern. We can use them to make predictions about what may happen in the future. Here are the basic trends reflected in line graphs and the language used to describe them.

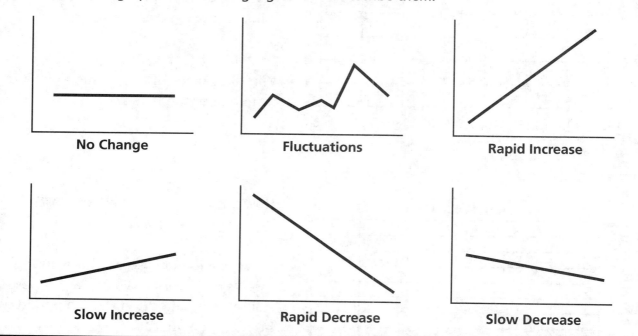

No Change   **Fluctuations**   **Rapid Increase**

Slow Increase   **Rapid Decrease**   **Slow Decrease**

Look at each graph. Label the trend or trends you see.

1

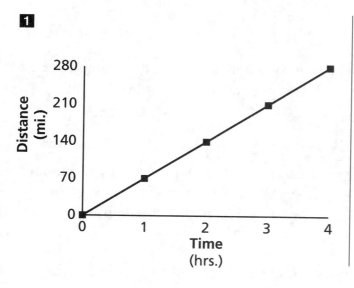

2

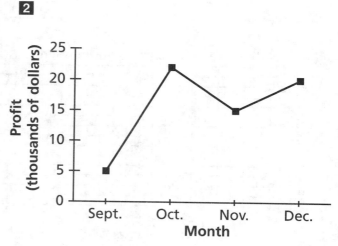

Probability and Statistics © 2005 Creative Teaching Press

Continue to page 2.

Trends

Page 2

3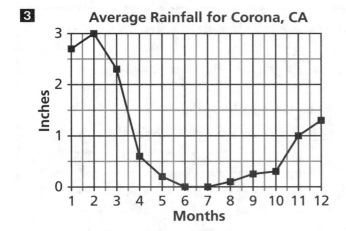

Average Rainfall for Corona, CA

5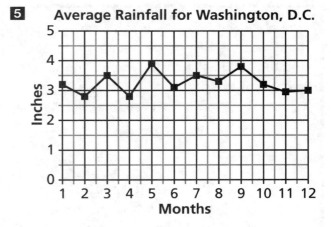

Average Rainfall for Washington, D.C.

4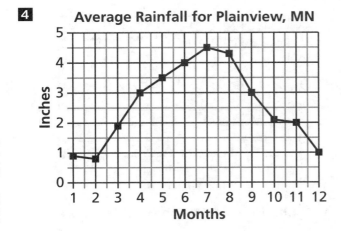

Average Rainfall for Plainview, MN

6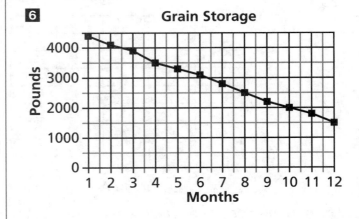

Grain Storage

Intervals
Reading and Writing Line Graphs

The choice of increments can alter the appearance of the data. These two graphs use the same data, but the first graph manipulates it in such a way that the long period with no increase during the 1980s is almost invisible. The second graph uses uniform intervals, so it gives a clearer picture of the situation.

The Federal Hourly Minimum Wage Since Its Inception

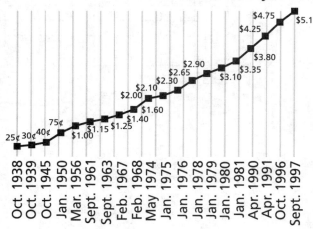

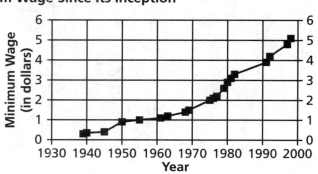

Compare the graphs. Answer the questions.

1

People Convicted of Crimes in Carsonville

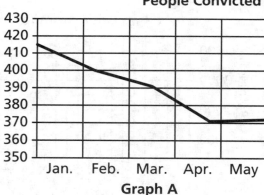

Graph A

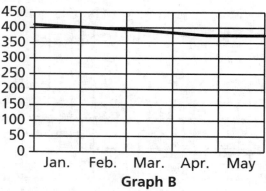

Graph B

Both graphs present accurate information with a regular interval. Which would you present if you wanted to argue that the city needs to increase funding for more police officers? Which would you present if you wanted to congratulate the existing police officers on a job well done?

Continue to page 2.

Probability and Statistics © 2005 Creative Teaching Press

Intervals
Page 2

Here are some tips for making intervals:

1 Find the range for both the data and the time period over which the data was gathered.

2 Divide the range into manageable intervals.

For example:

- If your data was collected over ten years, you wouldn't want to show every month. That would be an enormous graph. You'd show every six months or every year.
- If you have 20 pieces of data, all between 0 and 1 (e.g., 0.25, 0.32), then you wouldn't have intervals of whole numbers. The dots would be too close together to read. Instead, you would divide your intervals into tenths (e.g., 0, 0.1, 0.2, 0.3).

Examine the data. Number and label the X- and Y-axis.

2 Henry's weight (kg): 1991, 68; 1992, 70; 1993, 74; 1994, 74; 1995, 73; 1996, 76

Probability and Statistics © 2005 Creative Teaching Press

Name _____   Date _____

Starting from Zero
Creating Line Graphs

To create a line graph . . .
- Be clear about the relationship you want to show. Do you have enough data to show that relationship? If not, further research may be required.
- Use the range to plan out reasonable, regular intervals on the X- and Y-axis.
- Label your graph as completely and clearly as possible.
- If your graph is part of a report you will be presenting, use bright-colored points and lines for easy reading.

Graph each set of data.

1   **Gas Volume**

Temperature (°C)	Volume (mL)
100	317
80	297
60	288
40	278
30	252
10	236
0	233
-10	227
-30	202

Probability and Statistics © 2005 Creative Teaching Press

Continue to page 2.

Starting from Zero
Page 2

2 **Distance Traveled over Time**

Time (sec.)	Distance (m)
0	0
1	2
2	8
3	18
4	32
5	50
6	72
7	98
8	128
9	162
10	200

3 **Atomic Numbers and Related Energy**

Atomic Number	Ionization Energy (volts)
2	24.46
4	9.28
6	11.22
8	13.55
10	21.47

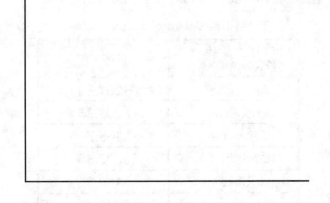

Graph Practice I
Review

Remember: Label your graphs as completely as possible.

Solve.

1 Use the data to create a line graph.

Changes in Water Temperature

Minutes	Temperature (°C)
0	48
1	45
2	41
3	39
4	35
5	32
6	31
7	30
8	29
9	29
10	28

2 Use the data to sketch a bar graph.

Total Daily Travel Allowances

Employee's Home City	Amount
Adelaide	$207.35
Brisbane	$201.35
Canberra	$185.35
Darwin	$202.35
Hobart	$189.35
Melbourne	$235.35
Perth	$202.35
Sydney	$238.35

Probability and Statistics © 2005 Creative Teaching Press

Graph Practice II
Review

Solve.

1 Look at the two graphs.

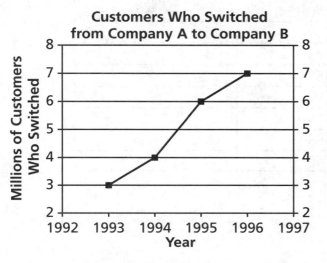

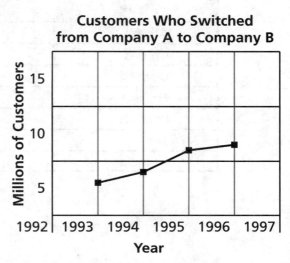

How are they different? How are they alike? Which graph would look better in a Company A board meeting?

2 Look at the two graphs.

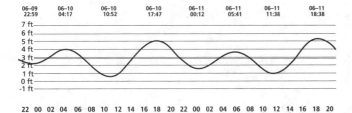

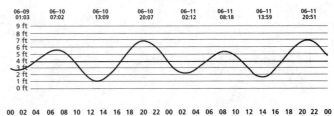

How are they alike? How are they different? On the evening of June 10, which beach experienced high tide first? Which beach seems to have a greater range of sea level as the tides change?

Graph Practice III
Review

Use the table to construct a pie graph.

Roses Sold

Type	No. Sold	% of Whole
Albas	14	
Chinas	43	
Damask	68	
Noisettes	97	
Portland	15	
Tea	65	
Galacia	40	

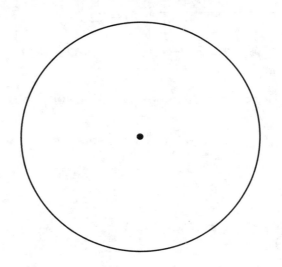

Name _____   Date _____

Histo-What?
Understanding Histograms

A **histogram** is bar graph in which each bar represents an interval rather than a specific value.

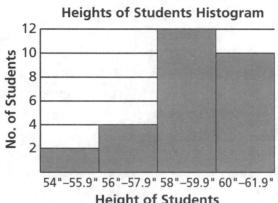

Heights of Students Histogram

With the histogram displaying the heights of students, we can determine that the following is true:

• There are 2 students between 54 and 55.9 inches.
• There are 4 students between 56 and 57.9 inches.
• There are 12 students between 58 and 59.9 inches.
• There are 10 students between 60 and 61.9 inches.
• Adding up the totals, we know there are 28 students.

Read each histogram, and answer the questions.

1

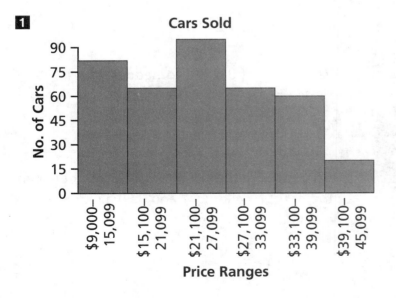

Cars Sold

Which price range was the most popular?

Which price range was the least popular?

How many cars were sold in the $33,100–39,099 price range?

Continue to page 2.

Histo-What?
Page 2

2

Computers Sold

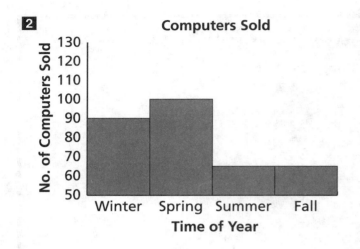

Which season has the highest volume of computer sales?

What was the difference in the number of computers sold in the winter and spring?

On average, how many computers are sold in a season?

3

Number of Tornadoes by Time of Day in Oklahoma 1950–1995

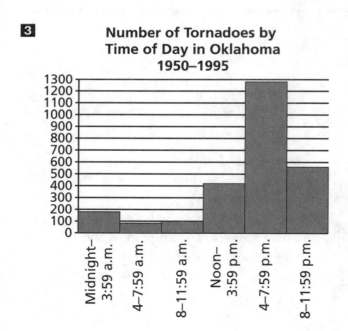

At what time of the day is it most likely that a tornado will occur?

What time of day are tornadoes least likely to occur?

How many more tornadoes occurred between the hours of midnight and 3:59 a.m. than 4 a.m. and 7:59 a.m.?

Probability and Statistics © 2005 Creative Teaching Press

The History of It
Determining Histogram Intervals

To determine intervals, calculate the range of the data, decide on the number of intervals you want to have, and divide the range by the number of intervals. If that isn't a whole number, adjust the number of intervals until the range is a multiple of that number.

Determine equal intervals for each set of data.

1 **Data:** 55, 58, 60, 43, 53, 84, 79, 65, 49, 63, 68, 45, 86, 79

Possible Intervals:

2 **Data:** 4.5, 4.7, 8.6, 7.3, 5.9, 6.0, 5.0, 8.7, 5.5, 6.7, 8.1, 7.8, 5.6

Possible Intervals:

3 **Data:** 6.899, 7.567, 4.567, 3.456, 7.555, 6.897, 6.895, 4.777, 6.888, 4.587, 5.876, 7.124, 5.923, 6.543, 7.865, 7.678

Possible Intervals:

4 **Data:** 987, 678, 567, 878, 998, 457, 876, 856, 786, 567, 786, 700, 650, 600, 879

Possible Intervals:

Probability and Statistics © 2005 Creative Teaching Press

Name _____ Date _____

Relatively Speaking
Understanding Relative Frequency Histograms

Relative Frequency Histogram: a histogram where the bar represents the proportion of the data in that interval of the graph compared to the total set of data represented in the graph. To make a relative frequency histogram, you need to divide the number of data values in each interval by the total number of values in the data set. This will give you the proportion or frequency. Reviewing the previous histogram:

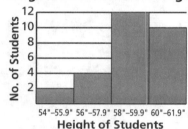

Heights of Students Histogram

For students between 54 and 55.9 inches, the frequency is 2/28 ≈ 0.07.
For students between 56 and 57.9 inches, the frequency is 4/28 ≈ 0.14.
For students between 58 and 59.9 inches, the frequency is 12/28 ≈ 0.43.
For students between 60 and 61.9 inches, the frequency is 10/28 ≈ 0.36.

Heights of Students Histogram

We construct the relative frequency histogram using the frequency values.

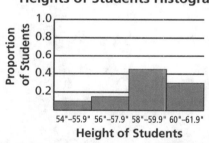

Use the data to complete the chart.

Babe Ruth's RBIs

Interval	Frequency	Relative Frequency
0–24.9	5	
25–49.9	0	
50–74.9	2	
75–99.9	2	
100–124.9	3	
125–149.9	5	
150–174.9	5	

Probability and Statistics © 2005 Creative Teaching Press

Histogram Intervals
Determining Histogram Intervals

Make sure that the intervals are all the same increments. The data cannot overlap. That is, you cannot have a column that is 5 to 10 and a column that is 10 to 20, because a data point of 10 could go in either column. One solution is to add tenths to the number and separate the intervals at 0.5 or 0.9.

Construct a histogram and a relative frequency histogram for each data set.

1 After a test on statistics, the teacher wrote the following data on the board that showed students' results: 81%, 77%, 98%, 100%, 88%, 68%, 82%, 79%, 95%, 98%, 75%, 76%, 87%, 98%, 100%, 67%, 94%, 98%, 92%, and 87%.

2 During a race, the coach recorded the following times in seconds for each participant: 15, 17, 16, 14, 13, 10, 12, 13, 11, 15, 20, and 24.

3 During a fitness test, the physical education teacher recorded how many sit-ups each student did: 100, 55, 49, 78, 95, 40, 67, 89, 46, 37, 67, 75, 92, 87, 79, 88, 86, 94, 101, 50, 66, 83, and 87.

4 At a local candy store, the cashier recorded the following transactions: $1.55, 80¢, $2.65, $1.95, $1.05, 75¢, 99¢, $1.15, 89¢, $2.00, $2.30, and $1.45.

Grouped Stats
Making Histograms

> **Remember:** Label your histogram as completely as possible. Choose intervals that show any differences as clearly as possible.

For each exercise, use the data to construct a histogram and a relative frequency histogram.

1 The ages of men and women polled who exercise 5 or more hours per week are as follows: 47, 18, 55, 66, 48, 25, 43, 70, 45, 44, 64, 50, 72, 27, 19, 51, 35, 35, 50, 70, 39, 63, 53, 28, 54, 62, 20, 51, 29, 21, 64, 33, 22, 34, 32, 59, and 24. (Hint: Use 60 and up for the last interval.)

2 The recorded times (in minutes) for completing a timed math test include: 20, 25, 39, 19, 25, 29, 18, 20, 37, 35, 34, 30, 30, 26, 27, 22, 25, 26, 34, 26, and 27.

Probability and Statistics © 2005 Creative Teaching Press

Continue to page 2.

Grouped Stats
Page 2

3 The following are weights (in pounds) of newborns: 7.5, 8.9, 9.1, 6.6, 5.8, 7.9, 8.0, 8.5, 8.2, 7.6, 6.9, 8.8, and 7.3.

4 These are the ages (in years) of dogs at the park: 2, 1, 0.5, 5, 7, 12, 3, 6, 2, 0.25, 3, 7, 4, 5, 5, 2, 1, 6, 11, 15, 0.75, 0.5, 4, 7, 12, 0.75, 9, 9, and 12.

Probability and Statistics © 2005 Creative Teaching Press

The Flea Market
Constructing Histograms

Remember: Label your histogram well.

Construct a histogram and a relative frequency histogram for each data set.

1 The percentage of purchases made at each booth by children between the ages of 8 and 14 include: 40%, 12%, 8%, 5%, 28%, 2%, 0.5%, 3%, 2%, 21%, 5%, 7%, 1%, 0.8%, 7%, 14%, 0.75%, 14%, 32%, and 4%.

2 The following are times (in minutes) that children wait until being served at a food booth: 15, 5, 8, 4, 14, 10, 12, 13, 7, 6, 7, 10, 14, 5, 4, 3, 6, 9, 9, 12, 11, 6, 3, 9, and 2.

Probability and Statistics © 2005 Creative Teaching Press

Continue to page 2.

The Flea Market
Page 2

3 These are the number of items on display at each booth: 100, 55, 19, 38, 95, 50, 72, 250, 125, 47, 114, 25, 92, 87, 67, 80, 86, 94, 143, 205, 66, 83, and 57.

4 A merchant recorded his transactions selling lemonade and homemade french fries: $1.75, $1.00, $0.75, $1.50, $2.50, $2.75, $1.00, $0.75, $1.50, $1.50, $2.50, $2.75, $2.50, $1.00, and $1.50.

Probability and Statistics © 2005 Creative Teaching Press

Statistics **137**

Dog Show
Review

Remember: Label your histogram well.

Construct a histogram and a relative frequency histogram for each data set.

1 Here are the heights (in inches) of dogs participating in obedience trials: 15, 20, 45, 65, 33, 42, 45, 24, 34, 21, 33, 36, 56, 45, 43, 44, 35, 42, 32, 52, 38, 49, 29, 41, 44, and 42.

2 The times (in seconds) that it takes drivers to pass through a tunnel include: 26, 49, 44, 28, 35, 36, 33, 35, 38, 37, 35, 31, 28, 29, 33, 32, 44, 42, 39, 35, 38, 33, 33, 36, 34, 35, 44, 29, 30, 43, and 40.

Probability and Statistics © 2005 Creative Teaching Press

Continue to page 2.

Dog Show
Page 2

3 The amounts spent at a souvenir booth include: $12.50, $42.10, $23.95, $33.60, $24.90, $15.20, $25.90, $35.65, $22.50, $44.60, $28.95, $35.60, $28.90, $16.20, $25.90, and $36.95.

4 The ages (in years) of the winning dogs at a dog show are as follows: 5, 2, 4.5, 3, 3.5, 4.5, 3, 4, 2, 5, 8, 3, 7, 4.5, 2.5, 5, 3, and 4.

Leaves
Reading Stem-and-Leaf Displays

Stem-and-leaf display: a method of organizing data in an increasing or decreasing order. A stem-and-leaf display is a lot like a histogram, where one value (most commonly the ones place of the data) functions as the bar. Each piece of data is "split" according to place value.

Weight Lifted

10	2
9	26
8	03457
7	0112224455556788
6	00001122333334444455566788999999
5	0001222344445555566677789999
4	000122234444555566777789999
3	0000011111366777888
2	224555789
1	24679

The numbers on the left side of the line are the tens values of the original data. The numbers on the right are the ones values. So the first three pieces of data at the top of the graph are 102, 92, and 96. We can see by looking at the data that most of the children who attempted to lift a weight lifted between 40 and 69 pounds. The 40, 50, and 60 bars are longer than all the other bars, and combined, they equal more than half of the total data.

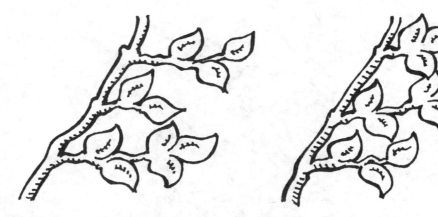

Continue to page 2.

Probability and Statistics © 2005 Creative Teaching Press

Leaves
Page 2

Read each display, and answer the questions.

1

8	024
7	0336778
6	00111335669
5	112445777777789999
4	333556778
3	33567
2	0224
1	89

What is the greatest data point?

What is the range?

What is the mode?

2

28	3
27	000033566
26	0003358889
25	5576
24	3354
23	000000012223
22	00033355788899
21	002224

What is the greatest data point?

What is the range?

What is the mode?

Probability and Statistics © 2005 Creative Teaching Press

Branching Out
Drawing Stem-and-Leaf Displays

First: Choose which place value will be the "leaf" and which will be the "stem."

Then: List the stems in a column in order from least to greatest or greatest to least. Draw a vertical line to separate the stems and leaves.

Finally: Go through the data, placing the correct leaf where it belongs for each value.

Data: 11, 41, 69, 87, 43, 54, 78, 56, 33, 45, 37, 66, 89, 98, 76, 56, 15, 55

- Identify the tens value for the stem and the ones value for the leaf.
- List the numbers 1 through 9 in order in a column. (You could also list 9 to 1 if you wanted to go in decreasing order.)
- Draw a line to the right of the stem numbers, and then fill in the leaves.

```
1 | 1   5
2 |
3 | 3   7
4 | 1   3   5
5 | 4   5   6   6
6 | 6   9
7 | 6   8
8 | 7   9
9 | 8
```

When making a stem-and-leaf display, line up the leaves with an equal distance between each so that the display is similar to a bar graph.

Organize the data in a stem-and-leaf display.

1 During one school week, a teacher recorded the number of questions asked in each of his classes every day. The numbers of questions asked was: 10, 15, 25, 15, 13, 14, 26, 28, 27, 15, 16, 14, 28, 19, 20, 18, 25, 15, 18, 29, 17, 13, 16, 20, and 24.

Probability and Statistics © 2005 Creative Teaching Press

"Natural" Statistics
Constructing Stem-and-Leaf Displays

```
8 | 9
9 | 8
7 | 6   8
6 | 6   9
5 | 4   5   6   6
4 | 1   3   5
3 | 3   7
2 |
```

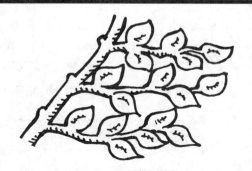

Create a stem-and-leaf display for each set of data.

1 **Data:** 1.23, 3.45, 2.34, 4.56, 7.65, 2.43, 3.42, 8.76, 5.22, 2.55, 1.99, 2.65, 6.43, 3.76

2 **Data:** 123, 456, 789, 478, 345, 678, 923, 567, 845, 673, 214, 543, 678, 677, 344

3 **Data:** 55.9, 54.0, 50.7, 52.6, 55.7, 59.6, 55.6, 53.7, 51.9, 57.8, 58.8, 54.6, 59.9

Two or More Samples
Comparing Graphs

Data is often collected from more than one sample to compare different groups. Males might be compared to females. An older generation might be compared to a younger generation. It is often easier to compare this information in graph form.

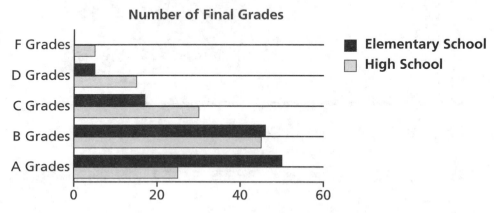

Number of Final Grades

The key to understanding this graph is in the key or legend. Before any of the bars make sense, we need to know what the black represents and what the gray represents. Once we know that the different colors represent different student groups, we can make the following statements based on the information:

1 More elementary students received an A.

2 About the same number of high-school and elementary students received a B.

Read the graph, and answer the questions on the next page.

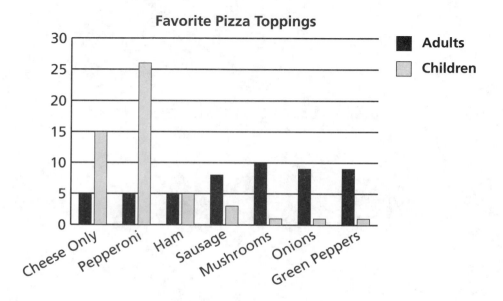

Favorite Pizza Toppings

Probability and Statistics © 2005 Creative Teaching Press

Continue to page 2.

Two or More Samples

Page 2

1. What is the favorite topping of the kids surveyed?

2. What is the favorite topping of the adults surveyed?

3. Would you say that adults and kids have similar tastes based on this graph? Why or why not?

4. If you were having a party with mostly adults as guests, what kind of pizza would you order to please them?

5. If you were having a party with mostly kids as guests, what kind of pizza would you order to please them?

6. Write two comparison statements that you could make based on the information in the graph.

Probability and Statistics © 2005 Creative Teaching Press

Program Results
Comparing Samples in a Bar Graph

Remember: Check the key or legend before trying to read a graph. You need to know what those color differences mean to properly read the graph.

Circle City Library began a new program in the summer to help cut back on overdue books. Patrons may now renew books online from home. You need to present a report to the library's board of directors tonight so it may decide whether to continue funding the program. Here is your graph:

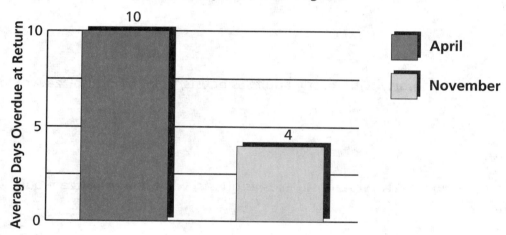

Effect of New Library Renewal Program

1 Does the program appear to be working?

2 Most books were about how many days overdue last April?

3 What is the typical number of days books were overdue in November?

4 Does the graph tell you whether there were more books checked out in November than in April?

5 What are two statements you can make about the new library program based on the information in the graph?

Probability and Statistics © 2005 Creative Teaching Press

Name _____ Date _____

Smoking Statistics
Comparing Pie Graphs

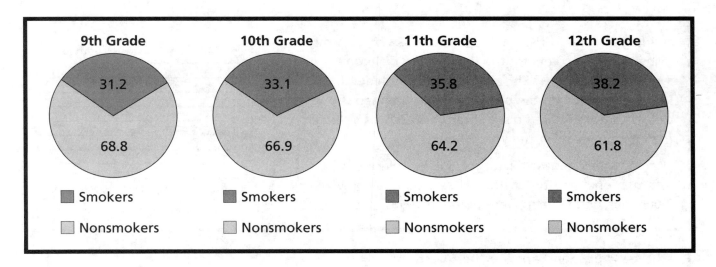

Examine the graphs above, and answer the questions.

1 By examining the graphs, what trend do you see as the student population ages?

2 What is the increase between ninth and tenth grade in the percentage of students who smoke? Between tenth and eleventh grade? Between eleventh and twelfth grade?

3 Between which grades do you see the greatest increase in smokers?

4 What is the average percentage of smokers for all grades?

5 Draw a pie graph to reflect your results from Question 4.

6 What is the percentage difference in high-school smokers between ninth and twelfth grade?

Twice the Information
Reading Line Graphs with Two Data Sets

A line graph can compare two or more sets of data by using different colors for the lines and/or different symbols for the lines. This requires a key or legend. In the graph above, the property being graphed shows clearly that there are no significant differences between men and women for the years shown.

Unfortunately, the writer forgot one key piece of information. The title! Without it, we do not know what 3,000 men and women were doing in 1996.

Read the graphs, and answer the questions.

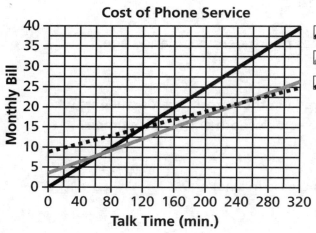

1 What relationship does the graph show?

2 Which company is represented by the solid light line?

3 How did you find the information to answer Question 2?

4 If you talk an average of 40 minutes per month, which plan gives the lowest rate?

5 If you talk an average of 320 minutes per month, which plan gives the lowest rate?

6 If your talk time varies greatly from month to month, which plan shows the least increase over time?

7 During which range of talk time is Company B the least expensive option?

Probability and Statistics © 2005 Creative Teaching Press

Milk!
Reading Line Graphs with Two Data Sets

U.S. Consumption of Milk per Person, 1909–2000

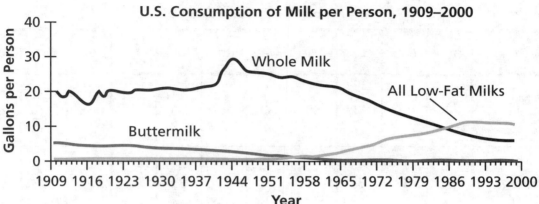

Use the graph above to answer the questions.

1 In about what year did low-fat milk consumption equal that of whole milk?

2 During what period of time did whole milk consumption peak?

3 What units are used to measure the milk consumption?

U.S. Consumption of Cheese per Person, 1909–2000

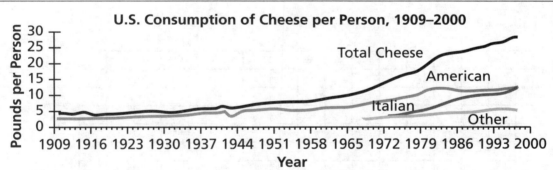

American cheeses include cheddar, Colby, cottage cheese, and Monterey Jack. Italian cheeses include mozzarella, ricotta, provolone, and Parmesan. Other cheeses include Swiss, cream cheese, Neufchatel, blue, Gorgonzola, and more.

Use the graph above to answer the questions.

4 What was happening in the United States around the early 1940s to cause that temporary decline in cheese consumption?

5 When did American consumption of Italian cheeses start?

6 Name two cheeses included in the American category.

Probability and Statistics © 2005 Creative Teaching Press

Plotting with Multiple Data Sets
Creating Line Graphs with Three Data Sets

Monthly Temperatures

Month	Jan.	Feb.	Mar.	Apr.	May	June	July	Aug.	Sept.	Oct.	Nov.	Dec.
Los Angeles	55	56	58	59	62	66	70	73	68	65	61	57
New Orleans	54	57	63	70	75	81	82	82	79	71	62	56
New York City	31	31	38	49	61	70	75	77	67	56	44	35

Use the chart above to plot a line graph that shows the average daily temperature for all three locations. Use a different colored pencil for each city. Be sure to create a key or legend.

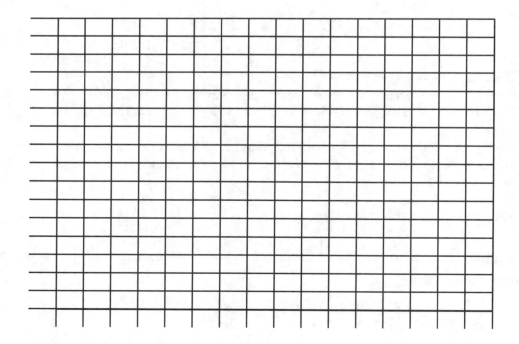

Probability and Statistics © 2005 Creative Teaching Press

Time, Temperature, and Humidity
Creating Line Graphs with Two Data Sets

Time	Temperature	Relative Humidity	Time	Temperature	Relative Humidity
7:02	82.9	76	9:17	84.6	74
7:17	82.8	77	9:32	85.3	73
7:32	83.1	77	9:47	85.3	73
7:47	83.08	76	10:02	85.4	72
8:02	83.08	76	10:17	86.7	71
8:17	84.2	76	10:32	86.7	70
8:32	84.4	75	10:47	86.7	71
8:47	84.4	75	11:02	88	69
9:02	84.07	74	11:17	87.8	68

Use the data to plot the temperature and relative humidity changes over time.

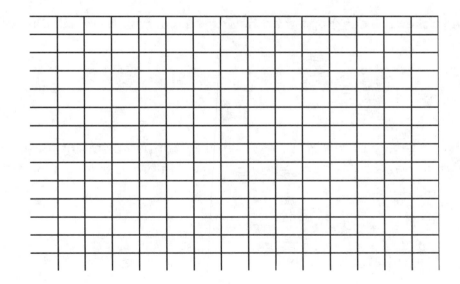

Is That Necessary?
Finding Relevant Data

Name	Gender	Age	Height (in.)	Weight (lb.)	Eye Color
Bob	male	63	70	200	brown
Steve	male	35	75	210	brown
Jessica	female	33	65	130	green
Michael	male	8	52	63	blue
Michelle	female	12	63	95	green

When analyzing data, keep in mind that some data will be relevant to the questions you have and some will not. It is important for you to determine which data is which.

If we were checking the correlation of age vs. weight, we would only need to include the sets of information from those two categories and make a scatter plot. We would discard the rest of the data.

Use the chart above to answer the questions.

1 You want to know the difference in age between the oldest and youngest person in this group. Which group of data would you use? What is another term for this calculation?

2 Use the data to sketch a bar graph that shows eye color results. Which data did you use?

3 What is the average age of this group? Which group of people might this group represent— a group of workers at a car factory, a group of seventh-grade students, or a family?

Probability and Statistics © 2005 Creative Teaching Press

Continue to page 2.

Is That Necessary?
Page 2

Determine which information is needed for each graph.

Data Set	A	B	C	D
Sample Size	100,000	153 (entire population)	100	578 (entire population)
Population	U.S. adult citizens	Math students in 7th and 8th grade at a school	Florida	North Elementary School
Facts	Age, political preference, state of residence	Gender, grade point average, weekly study hours	Age, number of hours in sun per week	Age, gender, favorite subject

4 You want to determine if people in Michigan and Ohio have similar political preferences. What data do you use?

5 You want to determine if a child's age affects their choice of a favorite subject at North Elementary School. What information do you use?

6 You want to find the average age of students at North Elementary School. What information do you use? How would you find the average?

7 You want to see if there is any correlation between the age and number of hours in the sun among Florida residents. What information do you use?

8 You want to determine if there is any correlation between weekly study hours and grade point averages. What information do you use?

9 You want to determine if there is a correlation between age and political preference. What information do you use?

Analyzing Graphs
Analyzing Graph Relevancy

Sometimes a page includes two or more related graphs. Check titles and labels carefully. For example, which graph can answer the question, How many library books were checked out in June 2002?

Both graphs have information for the month of June, but only the second graph will tell you about June 2002.

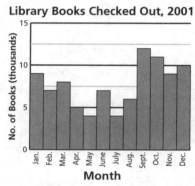

Library Books Checked Out, 2001

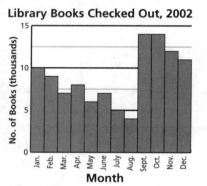

Library Books Checked Out, 2002

Use the graphs below to answer the questions.

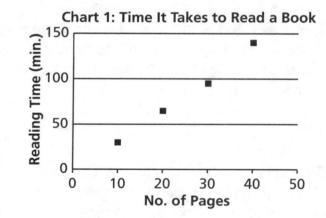

Chart 1: Time It Takes to Read a Book

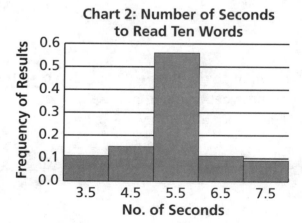

Chart 2: Number of Seconds to Read Ten Words

1 What is the most likely amount of time it would take to read ten words? Explain.

Which graph did you use?

2 Does the number of pages in a book have a linear correlation to the minutes it takes to read the book? Explain.

Which graph did you use?

3 Would you say it is likely for a person to read ten words in 15 seconds? Explain.

Which graph did you use?

Probability and Statistics © 2005 Creative Teaching Press

Name _____   Date _____

Book Purchases
Analyzing Relevant Data

Use the graphs below to answer the following statements.

Graph 1: Number of Books Read

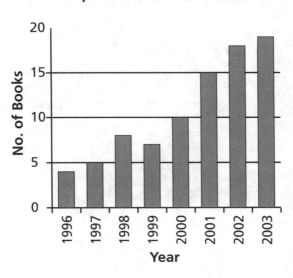

Graph 2: Number of Books Purchased (by Type)

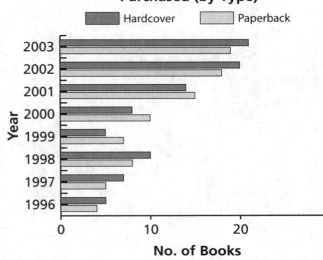

1 Would you say that people usually purchase hardcover or paperback books? Explain.

Which graph did you use?

2 If 25 people purchased hardcover books, how many people would probably purchase paperback books that same year? Explain.

Which graph did you use?

3 Do you think it is likely that 50 books were read in 1990? Explain.

Which graph did you use?

4 Do you think it is likely that out of 500 books purchased, 10 percent of them were hardcover and the rest were paperback? Explain.

Which graph did you use?

Name _____ Date _____

Statistics Crossword
Review

Complete the puzzle.

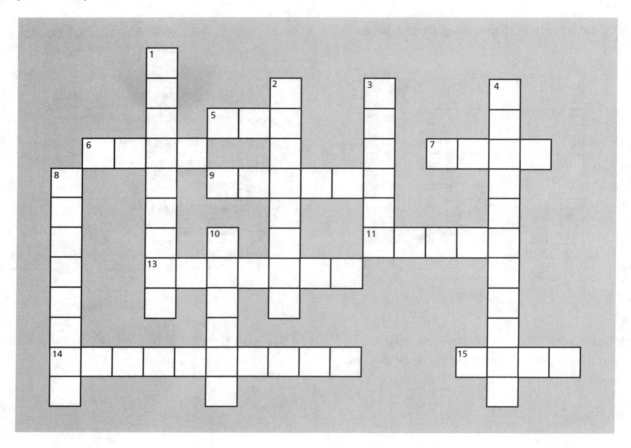

ACROSS

5. A well-defined collection of objects or numbers

6. Information

7. The average

9. A random set of the population

11. The difference between the least and greatest number

13. The sum of numbers divided by the quantity of numbers

14. The entire group or set from which you want data

15. The data value used most frequently

DOWN

1. A bar graph where the bars represent intervals

2. A _____-and-_____ display is a method of organizing data in order.

3. Scatter plots that form a line that is not vertical or horizontal are said to have _____ correlation.

4. A graph of two related properties

8. A graph that displays data visually or horizontally

10. The middle number of a data set

Probability and Statistics © 2005 Creative Teaching Press

Organize and Compare
Review

Solve.

1 Find the average, range, median, mean, and mode for the following data.
The number of minutes it takes for each student in the class to shower is: 10.6, 5.7, 6.8, 8.9, 6.1, 12.5, 4.0, 5.4, 6.6, 7.9, 10.4, 5.3, and 6.2.

Average:

Range:

Median:

Mean:

Mode:

2 On a separate piece of graph paper, organize the data from Problem 1 as a stem-and-leaf display.

3 On a separate piece of graph paper, organize the data from Problem 1 as a bar graph.

Scatter and Histogram
Review

Solve.

1 Display the following data as a scatter plot.

Age	Weight (lb.)
10	65
43	115
37	200
25	120
26	170
15	100
16	90
33	125

Is there linear correlation between age and weight?

2 Display the following data in a histogram and in a relative frequency histogram.
The results (in percentages) of scores an English test include: 85, 76, 98, 99, 92, 75, 62, 67, 83, 85, 89, 75, 73, 88, 91, 90, 59, 86, 88, 85, 79, and 68.

Reading Graphs
Review

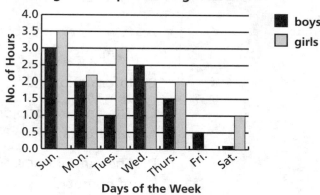

Average Time Spent Doing Homework

1 Use the graph to answer the questions. If there is not enough information in the graph to answer a question, indicate this by writing *N/A* (not applicable). Assume that the graph was obtained from accurate and random data.

a. How many students were surveyed?

b. On average, who spends more time doing homework?

c. What day is the biggest "homework day" overall?

d. Are there any major differences between the homework patterns of male and female students?

e. Write two statements based on the graph.

   •

   •

2 Pretend that you need to find the average number of hours a person watches television in the world. Your mom will let you call any telephone number you choose. You start randomly dialing. Is this a good random survey to answer the question? Why or why not?

Match It!
Review

For each vocabulary word, write the letter of the matching definition.

1 Average _____

2 Bar Graph _____

3 Data _____

4 Histogram _____

5 Linear Correlation _____

6 Mean _____

7 Median _____

8 Mode _____

9 Population _____

10 Range _____

11 Relative Frequency Histogram _____

12 Sample _____

13 Scatter Plot _____

14 Stem-and-Leaf Display _____

A. A well-defined collection of objects or numbers

B. Information

C. The entire group or set from which you want data

D. The sum of numbers divided by the amount of numbers

E. The middle number of the data

F. The data value used most frequently

G. A bar graph where the bars represent intervals

H. A random set of the population

I. A graph of two related properties on the XY axis

J. A frequently used bar graph

K. The difference between the least and greatest numbers

L. A graph displaying the data horizontally or vertically

M. The average

N. Two lines that correlate

O. Scatter plots that seem to form a line

P. A histogram where the bar represents the proportion of the data in that interval of the graph compared to the total set of data represented in the graph

Q. A method of organizing data in increasing or decreasing order

Probability and Statistics © 2005 Creative Teaching Press

More Graphs
Review

1 Find the average, range, median, mean, and mode for the following data set.
The number of canned goods collected by each student in the class was: 20, 15, 16, 36, 45, 8, 18, 16, 22, 14, 15, 16, 17, 10, 15, 16, 9, 30, 25, 41, 45, 42, and 37.

Average:

Range:

Median:

Mean:

Mode:

Draw any graphs on a separate sheet of graph paper. Clearly label your graphs, and be sure your name is on the graph paper.

2 Display the data of a plant's growth as a scatter plot.

Age (days)	Height (in.)
1	0
5	0.5
10	1.5
15	3
20	4
25	5

Is there linear correlation? _____

3 Organize the following data as a bar graph.
The average number of students absent from Country Academy each day is:
Monday, 2; Tuesday, 3; Wednesday, 1; Thursday, 1; and Friday, 2.

Graph It Out
Review

Solve.

1 Display the following data in a histogram and in a relative frequency histogram. The heights of students in centimeters include:

79	76	83	90
85	98	85	99
73	90	89	86
88	92	75	88
91	77	73	85
90	62	88	79
85	67	91	88

2 Pretend that you need to find the average number of calories a student in your school consumes in one 24-hour period. Explain a method you would use to find random and accurate data.

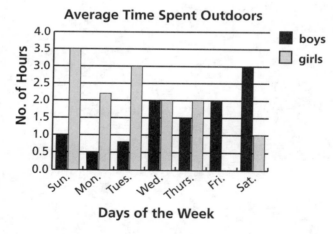

3 Use the graph to answer the questions. If there is not enough information in the graph to answer a question, indicate this by writing *N/A*. Assume that the graph was obtained from accurate and random data.

a. Based on the graph, on what day would you expect to find the most people outdoors?

b. How many people go outdoors on Saturdays?

c. What is the average number of hours per day spent outdoors for boys?

d. Would you say that the average time spent outdoors is similar for boys and girls? Explain.

Probability and Statistics © 2005 Creative Teaching Press

Last but Not Least
Review

Circle the correct response.

1 What type of graph would be best for determining if there is any type of correlation between pairs of data?

double bar graph   or   **scatter plot**

2 What place value is the stem in a stem-and-leaf display?

whole number   or   **decimal**   or   **depends on data**

3 There is always only one mode in a set of data.

true   or   **false**

4 The population and sample are sometimes the same.

true   or   **false**

5 What type of graph would you use if you want to compare two or more data sets?

double bar graph   or   **scatter plot**

Answer Key

Talk the Talk (page 6)

Experiment: Accept all reasonable responses.

1. Spinning a 1, 2, 3, or 4
2. 4
3. 2

Experiment: Accept all reasonable responses.

4. Spinning red, purple, black, blue, green, yellow, pink, or white
5. 8
6. green

Hop, Skip, Jump (pages 7–8)

Experiment: Accept all reasonable responses.

1. Landing on 1, 2, 3, 4, 5, 6, 7, 8, or 9
2. 9
3. 5
4. 9

Experiment: Accept all reasonable responses.

5. Landing on 1, 2, 3, 4, 5, 6, or 7
6. 7
7. 4
8. 2

Experiment: Accept all reasonable responses.

9. Landing on 1, 2, 4, 6, 8, 10, 12, 14, or 16
10. 9
11. 16
12. even

Experiment: Accept all reasonable responses.

13. 2, 3, 5, 7, 11, 13, 17, 20
14. 8
15. 7
16. prime

Roll It (pages 9–10)

Experiment: Accept all reasonable responses.

1. heads up, tails up
2. 2
3. heads up
4. No. You are just as likely to land tails up.

Experiment: Accept all reasonable responses.

5. Rolling a 1, 2, 3, 4, 5, or 6
6. 6
7. 5
8. Possible answer: Yes. Because it means not getting any of the other five possibilities ten times in a row.

Experiment: Accept all reasonable responses.

9. two heads up; two tails up; heads up and tails up
10. 3
11. heads up, tails up
12. There is an additional simple event.

Experiment: Accept all reasonable responses.

13. 1, 2, 3, 4, 5, 6, 7, 8, 9, 10, 11, or 12

14. 12
15. 10
16. You have twice as many simple events. You add the two faces together.

Likely or Lucky? (page 11)

1. Answers will vary. It is just as likely to get any other combination.
2. It is just as likely to get heads as tails.
3. Examine all possible outcomes.
4. Answers will vary.
5. They imply opposite meanings in probability.
6. Having an unlikely event occur is rare and, therefore, lucky.

Likely, Not Likely (pages 12–13)

1. Yes. If there are 20 people on the bus, and 12 more board, there are likely to be open seats on the 40-seat bus.
2. Not likely. If it was Carlos's turn two Fridays ago, then probably it will be three more Fridays before it is his turn again.
3. Ten years of no rain in August means it is likely to be another August day without rain.
4. No. The puppy usually digs two holes. It's likely that she will dig again.
5. No, it is not likely. Yes, it is possible.

How Likely? (pages 14–15)

1. 3/6 or 1/2
2. 2/6 or 1/3
3. 6/6; It's very likely. There are no other simple events.
4. 3/6 or 1/2   5. 1/6

So Far, So Good (pages 16–17)

1. 1/5   4. 4/10 or 2/5
2. 3/6 or 1/2   5. 2/12 or 1/6
3. 3/5

Is It Worth It? (pages 18–19)

1. 3/20   4. 8/20 or 2/5
2. 10/20 or 1/2   5. 3/5
3. 5/40 or 1/8   6. 1/15

Certainly Impossible (page 20)

1. Impossible. There aren't that many dots on a 9-dot domino.
2. Certain
3. Certain
4. Impossible. You can't choose a composite from a list of primes.

Real-Life Sample I (page 21)

Answers will vary. Invite students to share their responses.

Look Again (page 22)

1. We don't know what the other possibilities are or what sandwich ingredients are available.
2. We don't know how many other numbers are on the spinner or how much of the spinner the 6 takes up.
3. We don't know what the friend rolled, and we don't know how many sides are on the die.
4. We don't know how many dogs there are.
5. We don't know how many worms there are or how many critters there are altogether.

Marbles (page 23)

1. 6/20 or 3/10
2. 3/20
3. 5/20 or 1/4
4. 1/20
5. 5/20 or 1/4
6. 15/20 or 3/4
7. 0
8. 5/20 or 1/4
9. 9/20
10. 10/20 or 1/2

Next Step! (page 24)

1. 0.2
2. 0.25
3. 0.3
4. 0.4
5. 0.05
6. 0.05
7. 0.8
8. 0.8
9. 0.1
10. 1.0
11. 0.625
12. 0.4
13. 0.15
14. 0.08

Messy Decimals (page 25)

1. $0.\overline{33}$
2. $0.2\overline{77}$
3. $0.\overline{33}$
4. $0.\overline{55}$
5. $0.\overline{190476}$
6. $0.20\overline{833}$
7. $0.\overline{259}$
8. $0.1\overline{2}$
9. $0.\overline{33}$
10. $0.0\overline{925}$

Perfect Percents (page 26)

1. 20%
2. 25%
3. 30%
4. 5%
6. 5%
7. 80%
8. 80%
9. 10%
10. 100%
12. 40%
13. 15%
14. 8%

Approximate Percents (page 27)

1. 0.33; 33%
2. 0.28; 28%
3. 0.33; 33%
4. 0.56; 56%
5. 0.19; 19%
6. 0.21; 21%

7. 0.26; 26%
8. 0.12; 12%
9. 0.33; 33%
10. 0.09; 9%

Probability Percents (pages 28–29)

1. $2/6 = 0.\overline{33} \approx 0.33 \times 100 = 33\%$
2. $3/6 = 0.5 \times 100 = 50\%$
3. $4/6 = 0.\overline{66} \approx 0.67 \times 100 = 67\%$
4. $2/6 = 0.\overline{33} \approx 0.33 \times 100 = 33\%$
5. $1/8 = 0.125 \times 100 = 12.5\%$
6. $4/8 = 0.5 \times 100 = 50\%$
7. $6/8 = 0.75 \times 100 = 75\%$
8. $3/8 = 0.375 \times 100 = 37.5\%$
9. 3/5; 60%
10. 3/4; 75%
11. 1/20; 5%
12. 1/3; 33%

What Are the Chances? (pages 30–31)

1. 20%
2. 5%
3. 40%
4. 25%
5. 37.5%
6. 49%
7. 57.5%
8. green, clear
9. 1/10 or 10%; less
10. 3/20 or 15%; equal
11. 1/6 or 17%; more
12. 1/4 or 25%; more

Flip It! (page 32)

Answers will vary. Have partners check each other's math in the chart. Invite the class to discuss the final two questions.

Reality Check (pages 33–34)

Answers will vary. Have partners check each other's math in the chart.
1-2. Answers will vary.
3. Possible answer: This is not likely. The die is probably not fair.
4. This is likely. The probability of rolling a 6 out of 50 rolls is about 8 rolls, so 9 is reasonable.

Real-Life Sample II (page 35)

Answers will vary.

Spin It! (pages 36–37)

Answers will vary. Some students will find that their spinner does not spin freely, and this will affect the outcome.

Building Spinners (page 38)

1.

2.

3. Student response should begin with 4 branches. Each ends in 4 branches, each of which end in 4 branches, for a total of 64 possible outcomes. Four of these outcomes represents the desired outcome, for a likelihood of 4/64 or 1/16.

Real-Life Sample III (page 39)

Answers will vary. Encourage partners to check each other's work.

Once More, with Fractions (pages 45–46)

1. 1/9

2. $\frac{1}{3} \times \frac{1}{3} \times \frac{1}{3} = \frac{1}{27}$; $\frac{1}{27} + \frac{1}{27} + \frac{1}{27} + \frac{1}{27} + \frac{1}{27} + \frac{1}{27} + \frac{1}{27} = \frac{7}{27}$

3. $\frac{1}{2} \times \frac{1}{2} \times \frac{1}{2} = \frac{1}{8}$ 4. 1/27

5. 1/64

6. 1/3 × 1/3 × 1/3 × 1/3 × 1/3 = 1/243; 1/243 + 1/243 + 1/243 = 3/243 = 1/81

7. 1/9; 1/81; 1/729

Looking for Opposites (page 40)

1. Choosing a blue marble, a green marble, and an orange marble. (must include all three)
2. Not rolling a 1, or rolling a 2 through 6, or rolling a number greater than 1.
3. Not choosing a 4, or choosing a 1, 2, 3, and 5.
4. Having a girl.
5. Rolling the numbers less than or equal to 4.
6. Possible answers include: Determine if the event and the possible complement together make up all the possible simple events.

Not Equal (pages 47–48)

1. 1/12
2. 1/4
3. Possible answer: Spinning a 3 followed by a 3 is more likely than spinning a 1 followed by a 3. This makes sense because the space for a 3 is three times the space for the 1.
4. 1/16
5. 3/64
6. ~5%
7. 1/64
8. 1/8
9. ~2%, 12.5%
10. 1/12
11. 1/24
12. 33%

Nice Complement (page 41)

1. No. Because there is overlap.
2. NOT Event A.
3. NOT Event B.
4. Answers will vary. Possible answer:

Sketch It Out (page 42)

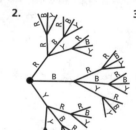 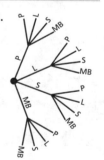 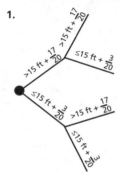

The Glider (pages 49–50)

1.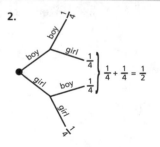

2. > 15 ft., > 15 ft. = $\frac{289}{400}$

> 15 ft., ≤ 15 ft. = $\frac{51}{400}$

≤ 15 ft., > 15 ft. = $\frac{51}{400}$

≤ 15 ft., ≤ 15 ft. = $\frac{9}{400}$

3. The glider flies a longer distance much more often than it flies the shorter distance. Joey should be satisfied in that regard.

Advanced Probability (pages 43–44)

1.    2.

A Combination of Things (pages 51–52)

1. 20 combinations: ROY, ROB, ROG, ROP, RYB, RYG, RYP, RBG, RBP, RGP, OYB, OYG, OYP, OBG, OBP, OGP, YBG, YBP, YGP, BGP

2. PL, PS, PG, PT, PC, LS, LG, LT, LC, SG, ST, SC, GT, GC, TC

3.

PH NH DH	PH DT QT	PT DT QH
PH NH DT	PT NH DH	PT DT QT
PH NH QH	PT NH DT	NH DH QH
PH NH QT	PT NH QH	NH DH QT
PH DH QH	PT NH QT	NH DT QH
PH DH QT	PT DH QH	NH DT QT
PH NT DH	PT DH QT	NT DH QH
PH NT DT	PT NT DH	NT DH QT
PH NT QH	PT NT DT	NT DT QH
PH NT QT	PT NT QH	NT DT QT
PH DT QH	PT NT QT	

How Many Ways? (pages 53–54)

1. 4, 5   5, 5
   4, 6   5, 6   6, 6; 1/21

2. 1/5

3. 1/56

4. TWs   SWs   JWs   TWl   SWl   JWl   TBs   SBs
   JBs   TBl   SBl   JBl; 1/12

Permutations (pages 55–56)

1. 24

2. 120

3. 24

4. 6

5. PND, PDN, PNQ, PQN, PDQ, PQD, NPD, NDP, NPQ, NQP, NDQ, NQD, DPN, DNP, DPQ, DQP, DNQ, DQN, QPN, QNP, QDP, QPD, QDN, QND

6. 6

   Note: You may choose to point out that three items always resulted in 6 permutations, four items resulted in 24, and five items resulted in 120. Or you may choose to have this discussion after the next exercise.

What Are the Chances of Order? (pages 57–58)

1. 1/24   4. 1/24

2. 1/120   5. 1/120

3. 1/6

Real-Life Sample IV (page 59)

Answers will vary. Encourage students to share their responses with the class.

Pickup Sticks (page 60)

1. 20/100 or 1/5   5. 2/100 or 1/50

2. 10/100 or 1/10   6. 32/100 or 8/25

3. 50/100 or 1/2   7. 1/4

4. 12/100 or 3/25   8. 1/20

Put On Your Thinking Cap (page 61)

1. 1/8

2. 1/4 (The first toss doesn't matter; it just sets whether you want heads or tails on the next two tosses.)

3. 1/36

4. 1/6 (If you don't specify a number, then all numbers are the desired outcome for the first roll [1/1]. You have a 1/6 chance of getting the [now specific] number on the second roll.)

5. We can only get a 1 and a 1 to sum to a value less than 3, so the answer is the same as Problem 3: 1/36.

6. There are a total of 36 possibilities for rolling the die two times. Twenty-one produce the desired outcome. Students can see this in a tree diagram. 21/36

7. Rule out the sums less than or equal to 6. There are 19 permutations we do not want. There are $6 \times 6 \times 6 = 216$ total permutations of three rolls. So there are $216 - 19 = 197$ permutations we do want. 197/216

Donuts (page 62)

1. Choosing glazed, plain, sprinkles, double chocolate, chocolate frosted, and jelly.

2.
> • glazed • plain • sprinkles
> • double chocolate • chocolate
> • frosted • jelly

3. 1/6

4. ~17%

5. 1/3

6. ~33%

7. NOT getting a plain donut

Jelly Beans (page 63)

1.

Color	Probability (fraction)	Probability (%)
White	1/10	10
Yellow	3/20	15
Red	1/4	25
Purple	11/50	22
Pink	17/100	17
Black	11/100	11

2. red   3. white

Six-Sided Die (page 64)

1. 6

2. Rolling a 1, 2, 3, 4, 5, and 6

3.
> • 1   • 2   • 3
> • 4   • 5   • 6

4. 1/6 or ~17%

5. 3/6 or 50%

6. Not rolling a 1 OR rolling a 2 through 6

Definitions (page 65)

1. B
2. H
3. K
4. C
5. G
6. Possible answer: Probability is using math to figure out how likely it is that something will happen. You can do an experiment to find the probability of the event. First, predict all the possible events that could happen. Those are the simple events. Then, decide which of those are the event you want and which are the complementary events. As you do the experiment, keep track of the results. These are written in your sample space.

Spinners and Chocolate (page 66)

1. We need to know the total number of marbles in the bag.
2. 7/20
3. We need to know if all the spinner spaces are equal.
4.

Sample and Population (page 67)

1. the average age at which a person can obtain a driver's license in the United States; whole
2. the gym could sell more memberships if it provided child care; part
3. what five-year-olds like to eat; part

So What? (pages 68–69)

Answers will vary. Possible answers include:

1. Not reasonable. It's a very small sample, and those people were already acting in a way that might cause them to lose weight.
2. Reasonable. The sample size is quite large, and the company gets random participants because the dentists choose the patients.
3. Not reasonable. The sample size is quite small and limited to one environment.
4. Reasonable. His sample is 2/3 of his population.

Stats and Facts (page 70)

1. Hypothesis: The doorway of the science room is too low.
   Data: height of doorways
   Population: the school doors
   Sample: the science wing doors
2. Hypothesis: All students would benefit from higher water fountains.
   Data: student heights
   Population: all students
   Sample: all boys

These results may be less accurate because they do not include any information about the average height of girls at the school.

3. Hypothesis: They skimped on the brown M&M's.
   Data: the percent of brown M&M's to the whole
   Population: bags of M&M's
   Sample: that bag of M&M's

   You can't assume anything about all bags of M&M's, because the sample size (one bag) is just too small.

Finding "Normal" (page 71)

1. 5 cm
2. 23
3. 27.5°C
4. 19
5. 51
6. 45.5'
7. 5
8. 5.3 in.
9. 874.5
10. 6.13

Convert Me (page 72)

1. 7.44 cm
2. 76.05 lb.
3. 18 L
4. 0.55
5. 3/6 or 1/2
6. 8.9$\overline{33}$ in.
7. 7/12
8. 66.8 min.

More Practice with Averages (page 73)

1. 7
2. 37.75
3. 3.76
4. 608
5. 58
6. 7.418
7. $1.32
8. 12.2°
9. 34
10. 4.05"

Fair Sample (pages 74–75)

1. Possible answer: We can't know for sure, but a class of advanced math students may not be a fair sample to represent all math students. Using one of the other math classes may represent a greater percentage of the students, but the best sample would be randomly choosing a few students from all five classes.
2. Accept all reasonable responses that support their answer with information related to sample size, relationship to the population, and/or accuracy.

Finding Facts (page 76)

Possible answers:

1. The Spanish-speaking population is not as well represented in Iowa as it is in some other states.
2. Florida's average temperatures far exceed the norms in much of the United States.
3. The school has a specific, limited population that includes implicit or implied age restrictions.
4. The average clothing size of a sumo wrestler is outside the norm for their age group.
5. The study isn't random. He's polling people who may be influenced by their friendship with him. In addition, the sample size is too small.

Next Step (page 77)

1. 63
2. 11
3. 64
4. 11,103
5. 8.82
6. 10/12 or 5/6
7. $6.48
8. 9.71
9. 27/40; **Hint:** Have students find the largest (7/8) and smallest (1/5) fractions, and find the LCD of those two only.
10. Possible answer: A large range may not be as reliable.

Great Range (page 78)

1. 59 ft.
2. 879 words
3. 77 lb., 14 oz.
4. 12.31 in.
5. 13 sec.
6. 47 cm

Greater Range (page 79)

1. average: 29 students
   range: 7 students
2. average: 6.7 hrs.
   range: 7 hrs.
3. average: 6 students (Round up. You can't have part of a student.)
   range: 9 students
4. average: 48.3 min.
   range: 100 min.
5. average: 10 min. and 47 sec.
   range: 1 hr., 4 min., 38 sec.

Personal Averages (page 80)

Answers may vary. Encourage students to share their responses with the class.

This 'n' That (pages 81–82)

1. average: 44.65 lb.
   range: 10.6 lb.
2. average: 20 students
   range: 7 students
3. Possible answer: The youngest class is likely to have the least amount of disposable income and be most dependent on others to drive. These are factors that would influence their attendance. A more reliable result would be a random sample of an English class from each grade level.
4. Possible answer: The population is the group you want to know about. The sample is the part of that group from which you actually gather data.
5. Convert it to a common unit of measurement.
6. There were no women included in the sample, but there are women included in the population. The medication might work differently on women.

7. average: 84 aphids
   range: 19 aphids
8. average: $3.60
   range: $1.00

Put It in Order (page 83)

1. from greatest to least or least to greatest
2. in chronological order
3. from greatest to least or least to greatest
4. from greatest to least or least to greatest; may convert to common denominator first
5. from greatest to least or least to greatest
6. from greatest to least or least to greatest

The Three Ms (pages 84–85)

1. 79.1%; 82%; 98%
2. 13 min.; 12 min.; 12 min.
3. 5.5; 6; 6
4. ~44.3 min.; 40 min.; 30 min.
5. Class A—84, 85, 85; Class B—70, 90, 95. Possible answer: When the mean, median, and mode are close together, the data is said to be more evenly distributed. The large range in Class B points out the three low scores that bring down the class average.

Mmmm (page 86)

1. 10; 9; 9 and 12
2. 0.455; 0.445; all values
3. 3 3/4"; 2 7/8"; all values
4. 25; 23; 30
5. 17,110; 17,423; all values
6. $62.00; $44.00; $44.00

The Parade (pages 87–88)

1. 4-H, ABC Day Care, Boy Scouts, Girl Scouts, Larson's Drug, Acme Hardware, Central Farm Co-Op, Central High Marching Band, Bob's Feed and Grain
2. average = 4; mode = 0 or 2
   Helen knows that the 4-H float is skewing the average and making it seem that there are about four animals on each float. The mode of 0 or 2 tells the judges that most floats have very few animals on them.
3. average = 1.92 tons. The parade committee does not have to pay the special tax.
4. 20 people

The Bars Show and Tell (pages 89–90)

1. Friday and Saturday
2. Thursday
3. No
4. seventh graders
5. 35–39
7. 85+
6. Have students find the difference between this year and 1997, and then add that number to the 1997 data.

Money! (page 91)

1. sports at Central High
2. Average Participation Fees of Boys Sports at Central High
3. football; $70
4. lacrosse; $20
5. ~$51
6. soccer and baseball, $40; swimming and gymnastics, $65
7. $60
8. $125
9. $25
10. lacrosse, soccer, basketball, or baseball ALSO lacrosse and soccer or lacrosse and baseball

Graph Ranges (pages 92–93)

Accept all reasonable responses. Possible answers include:

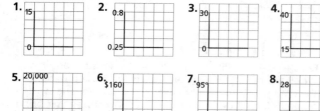

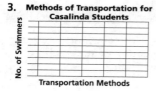

Label It (pages 94–95)

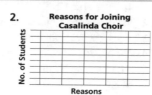

Choose an Increment (pages 96–97)

Answers will vary. Possible answers include:

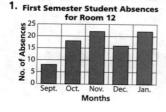

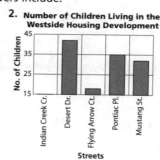

Creating a Bar Graph (pages 98–99)

Answers will vary. Possible answers include:

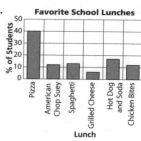

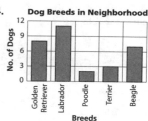

Real-Life Graphing I (page 100)

Answers may vary. Encourage students to share their responses with the class.

I See Dots (pages 101–102)

1. No. Vertical line indicates no correlation.
2. Yes. X increases as Y increases OR X decreases as Y decreases.
3. Yes. X increases as Y decreases OR X decreases as Y increases.
4. No; random

Plotting Points (pages 103–104)

Answers will vary. Possible answers include:

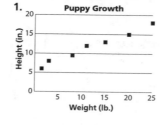

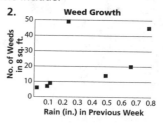

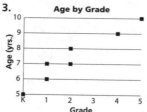

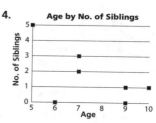

5. Age by Number of Siblings

A Good Plot (pages 105–106)

Answers will vary. Possible answers include:

1.

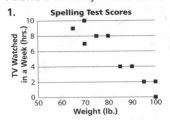

Spelling Test Scores

2.

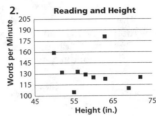

Reading and Height

3.

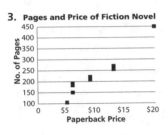

Pages and Price of Fiction Novel

4.

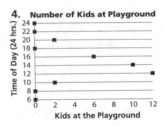

Number of Kids at Playground

5. Reading and Height

More Dots (page 107)

Possible answer:

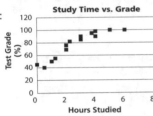

Study Time vs. Grade

There appears to be a correlation. Students who studied longer got better grades.

Real-Life Graphing II (page 108)

Answers will vary. Encourage students to share their responses with the class.

Show Me (pages 109–110)

Answers will vary. Possible answers include:

length—mean = 12.3 in.; median = 13 in.; mode = all values
weight—mean = 11 oz.; median = 12 oz.; mode = all values
Possible: bar graphs and scatter plot

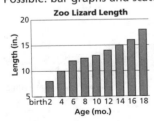

Zoo Lizard Length

Zoo Lizard Weight

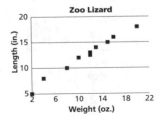

Zoo Lizard

Pie in the Sky (page 111)

1. a. Labrador Retriever

b. 5%

c. German Shepherd

d. Possible answer: It's a reasonable assumption, but it can't be proven since the total of "Other" still exceeds the German Shepherd.

e. Schnauzer and Yorkshire Terrier

2. a. Hispanic

b. 60%

c. American Indian/Alaskan

d. 2/3

Pies and Percents (pages 112–113)

1.

Favorite Sports

Sport	No. of People	% of Whole
Swiming	6	14%
Football	18	42%
Soccer	12	28%
Baseball	2	7%
Basketball	4	9%

2.

Points Earned This Weekend

Team	Points Earned	% of Whole
San Francisco	16	14%
Los Angeles	22	20%
Chicago	28	25%
Phoenix	31	28%
Baltimore	15	13%

3.

Hours Spent Cleaning This Week

Room of House	Hrs. Spent Cleaning	% of Whole
Bedroom	11	48%
Dining Room	2	9%
Kitchen	7	30%
Living Room	2	9%
Library	1	4%

4.

Canadian Elections 2000

Party	No. of Seats	% of Whole
Liberal	172	57%
Bloc Québécois	38	13%
Reform/Cdn. Alliance	67	22%
New Democratic Party	12	4%
Progressive Conservative	12	4%
Independent	0	0%

5.

Share of Peltville County Cheese Market

Seller	Units Sold	% of Whole
Big Mart	580	6%
Joe's Market	212	2%
Henrietta's Cheese Mkt.	1562	16%
Cheese R Us	1812	19%
Cheese World	5521	57%

Decimal Pie (page 114)

Favorite Ice Cream

Flavor	No. of People Who Named the Flavor	% of Whole
Vanilla	15	22
Chocolate	22	32
Strawberry	10	15
Neopolitan	6	9
Other	15	22

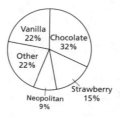

More Pie Graphs (page 115)

Bikes Sold This Week

Model	No. Sold	% of Whole
White Lightning	20	39
Silver Streak	12	24
Red Range	4	8
Mountain	15	29

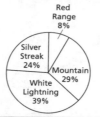

Apple Pie (page 116)

Apples Sold

Type	No. Sold	% of Whole
Red Delicious	200	22
Golden Delicious	350	39
Granny Smith	175	20
Jonathan	50	5
Winesap	55	6
McIntosh	70	8

Pumpkin Pie (page 117)

Pumpkins Sold

Type	No. Sold	% of Whole
Aspen	14	3
Harvest Moon	62	11
Jack-o'-Lantern	267	49
Happy Jack	25	5
Cinderella	150	28
Chelsey	8	1
Howden Field	15	3

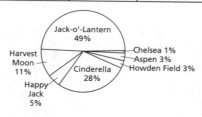

Line Graphs! (pages 118–119)

1. 29 in.; ~2 in.; 16 in.
2. between 0 and 2 months; 20 and 22 months
3. the federal minimum wage; no; the unit of measurement of money (dollars? cents? ten dollars?)

4. 2 hrs.; riding up between 20 and 60 min., riding down between 60 and 80 min.
5. This is probably a record of a large cafeteria. It would be unlikely for a single family to consume 12 lb. of peanut butter in a single month./ The summer. Each month had half the consumption of many of the other months./ December. Consumption might have been affected by the winter holidays.

Trends (pages 120–121)

1. rapid increase
2. fluctuations
3. rapid decrease followed by slow increase
4. rapid increase followed by rapid decrease
5. fluctuations
6. rapid decrease

Intervals (pages 122–123)

1. Graph A; Graph B
2.

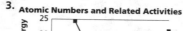
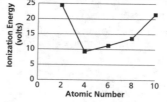

Starting from Zero (pages 124–125)

1.

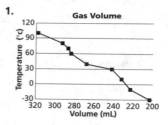

2.

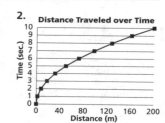

3.

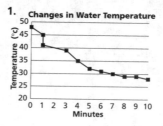

Graph Practice I (page 126)

1.

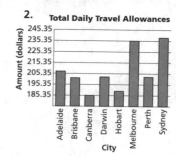

2.

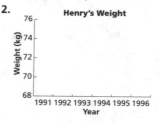

Graph Practice II (page 127)

1. The intervals are different./ The data is the same./ You would want to show the second graph at the Company A board meeting to downplay the changes.

2. They both describe the tides at a location on the West Coast./ The measurements are different./ Long Beach, Middle Harbor, California, experienced high tide first./ Eureka, Humboldt Bay, California, has the greater range of sea level.

Graph Practice III (page 128)

Roses Sold

Type	No. Sold	% of Whole
Albas	14	4
Chinas	43	13
Damask	68	20
Noisettes	97	28
Portland	15	4
Tea	65	19
Galacia	40	12

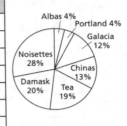

Histo-What? (pages 129–130)

1. $21,100–27,099; $39,100–45,099; 60
2. spring; 10; 72.5
3. 4–7:59 p.m.; 4–7:59 a.m.; ~90 tornadoes

The History of It (page 131)

Answers will vary. Possible answers include:

1. intervals of 5: 40, 45, 50, 55, 60, 65, 70, 75, 80, 85, 90
2. intervals of 0.5: 4.5, 5.0, 5.5, 6.0, 6.5, 7.0, 7.5, 8.0, 8.5, 9.0
3. intervals of 0.9: 3.400, 4.300, 5.200, 6.100, 7.000, 7.900
4. intervals of 100: 400, 500, 600, 700, 800, 900, 1,000

Relatively Speaking (page 132)

Babe Ruth's RBIs

Interval	Frequency	Relative Frequency
0–24.9	5	0.23
25–49.9	0	0
50–74.9	2	0.09
75–99.9	2	0.09
100–124.9	3	0.14
125–149.9	5	0.23
150–174.9	5	0.23

Histogram Intervals (page 133)

Answers will vary. Possible answers include:

1.
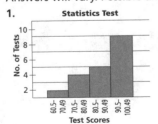
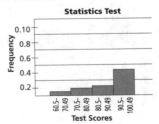

2.
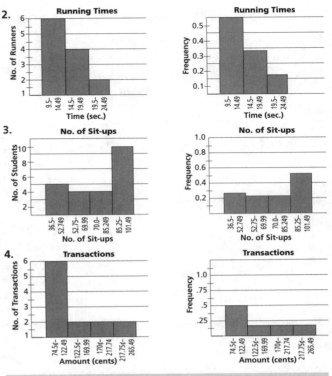

3.

4.

Grouped Stats (pages 134–135)

Answers will vary. Possible answers include:

1.
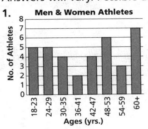
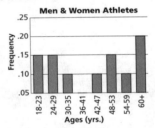

2.
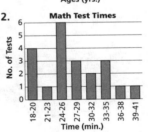
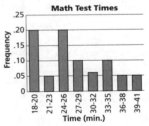

3.
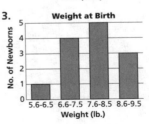
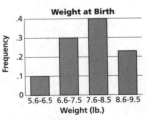

4.

The Flea Market (pages 136–137)

Answers will vary. Possible answers include:

1.

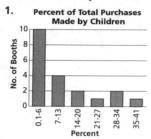

Percent of Total Purchases Made by Children

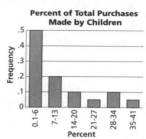

Percent of Total Purchases Made by Children

2.

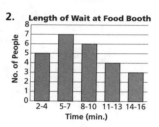

Length of Wait at Food Booth

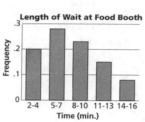

Length of Wait at Food Booth

3.

Number of Items on Display

Number of Items on Display

4.

Transactions at the French Fry Booth

Transactions at the French Fry Booth

Dog Show (pages 138–139)

1.

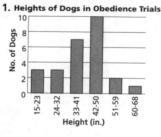

Heights of Dogs in Obedience Trials

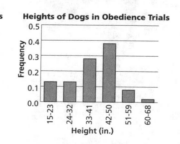

Heights of Dogs in Obedience Trials

2.

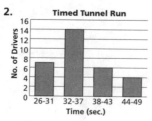

Timed Tunnel Run

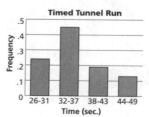

Timed Tunnel Run

3.

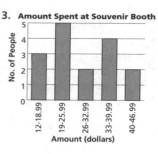

Amount Spent at Souvenir Booth

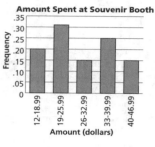

Amount Spent at Souvenir Booth

4.

Winning Dogs

Winning Dogs

Leaves (pages 140–141)

1. 84; 66; 57   **2.** 283; 73; 230

Branching Out (page 142)

Answers will vary. Possible answers include:

1.

```
1 | 0 3 3 4 4 5 5 5 6 6 7 8 8
2 | 0 0 4 5 5 6 7 8 8 8 9
```

"Natural" Statistics (page 143)

Answers will vary. Possible answers include:

1.
```
1 | 23 99
2 | 34 43 55 65
3 | 56
4 | 56
5 | 22
6 | 43
7 | 65
8 | 76
```

2.
```
1 | 23
2 | 14 34
3 | 44 45
4 | 56 78
5 | 43 67
6 | 73 77 78 78
7 | 89
8 | 45
9 | 23
```

3.
```
50 | 7
51 | 9
52 | 6
53 | 7
54 | 0 7
55 | 7 9 6
56 |
57 | 8
58 | 8
59 | 6 9
```

Two or More Samples (pages 144–145)

1. Pepperoni

2. Mushrooms

3. No. There were significant differences in all categories.

4. Possible answer: veggie pizza

5. Possible answer: pepperoni and cheese

6. Possible answer: More adults may prefer vegetables on pizza. About the same number of adults as kids prefer ham.

Program Results (page 146)

1. Yes

2. 10

3. 4

4. No

5. Possible answer: The new library program may reduce the number of days that books are overdue. Books in November were overdue less than half as many days as they had been the previous April.

Smoking Statistics (page 147)

Answers will vary. Possible answers include:

1. More teens take up smoking.

2. 0.9; 2.7; 2.4

3. between 10th and 11th grades

4. 34.58%

5.

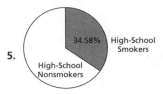

6. 7%

Twice the Information (page 148)

1. the increase in your phone bill the longer you talk on the phone

2. Company B

3. on the key or legend

4. Company A

5. Company C

6. Company C

7. 80 to 240 min.

Milk! (page 149)

1. ~1988

2. early to mid-1940s

3. gallons per person

4. World War II

5. ~1970

6. Possible answers include: cheddar and colby.

Plotting with Multiple Data Sets (page 150)

Answers will vary. Possible answers include:

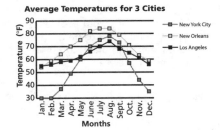

Time, Temperature, and Humidity (page 151)

Answers will vary. Possible answers include:

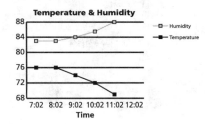

Is That Necessary? (pages 152–153)

1. age; range

2. eye color

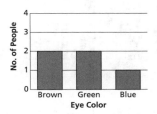

3. 30.2; The family is most likely. The data may show a grandfather, a married couple, and their two children. The children are too young to be workers. The adults are too old to be middle-school students.

4. Use part of A (political preference) with correct states. You could use a bar graph or histogram.

5. Use part of D (age and favorite subject). You could use a multiple bar graph.

6. Use part of D (age). You would take the sum of all the ages and divide by the number of students.

7. Use all of C. You could create a scatter plot.

8. Use part of B as a sample (omit gender). You could create a scatter plot.

9. Use part of A (omit state). You could create a multiple bar graph.

Analyzing Graphs (page 154)

1. 5.5 to 6.5 seconds/ It has the largest interval./ Chart 2

2. Yes. It is increasing at a similar rate./ Chart 1

3. No; less than 15/ That period is so large it's not on the graph./ Chart 1

Book Purchases (page 155)

1. About the same, because there aren't any really strong results./ Chart 2

2. About 25, because the numbers are similar each year./ Chart 2

3. No. The number of books read decreases approaching 1990./ Chart 1

4. No, because there isn't a big difference between the number of each type purchased in any years./ Chart 2

Statistics Crossword (page 156)

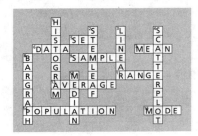

7. E   11. P

8. F   12. H

9. C   13. I

10. K   14. Q

Organize and Compare (page 157)

1. ~7.42; 8.5; 6.6; ~7.42; all

2.
```
 4 | 0
 5 | 3 4 7
 6 | 1 2 6 8
 7 | 9
 8 | 9
 9 |
10 | 4 6
11 |
12 | 5
```

3.

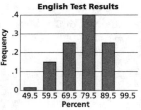

Scatter and Histogram (page 158)

1. ; no

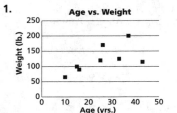

2.

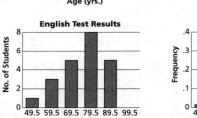

Reading Graphs (page 159)

1. a. N/A

b. similar

c. Sunday

d. No

e. Possible answer: Girls seem to study more. Boys seem to study more on Fridays.

2. No; Possible answer: Many areas of the world have poor to no phone service, and the sample you could get by yourself would be extremely small.

Match It! (page 160)

1. M, D   4. G

2. L   5. O

3. B   6. M, D

More Graphs (page 161)

1. ~23.2; 37; 16.5; ~23.2; 16

2. ; yes

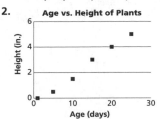

3.

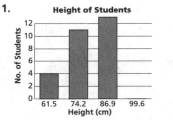

Graph It Out (page 162)

1.

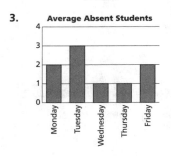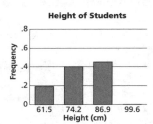

2. Possible answer: Randomly select students by having a program choose student ID numbers for you. Collect data from those students about what they eat for a week.

Randomly choose one day's data from each student. Calculate the calories, add up all the calories, and divide by the number of participating students.

3. a. N/A

b. N/A

c. ~1.5 hrs.

d. The amount of time is similar, but according to the graph, females are more likely to be outdoors at the beginning of the week, and males are more likely to be outdoors at the end of the week.

Last but Not Least (page 163)

1. scatter plot   4. true

2. depends on data   5. double bar graph

3. false